REVISE GCSE
Physical Educati⊘
PRACTICE
PAPERS

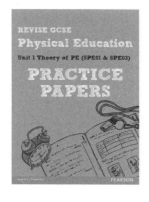

THE REVISE SERIES
Available in print or online

Online editions for all titles in the Revise series are available from Spring 2014.

Presented on our ActiveLearn platform, you can view the full book and customise it by adding notes, comments and weblinks.

Print edition

Revise GCSE PE Practice Papers   9781292013770

Online edition

Revise GCSE PE Practice Papers   9781292013787

These Practice Papers are designed to complement your classroom and home learning, and to help prepare you for the exam. They do not include all the content and skills needed for the complete course. They are designed to work in combination with the Revise Edexcel GCSE Physical Education Revision Guide and Workbook and Pearson's main GCSE Physical Education 2009 series.

For the full range of Pearson revision titles across GCSE, BTEC and AS Level visit:
www.pearsonschools.co.uk/revise

ALWAYS LEARNING   PEARSON

Contents

A small bit of small print

Awarding Organisations publish Sample Assessment Material and the Specifications on their websites, this is the official content. The questions in this book have been written to help you practise what you have learned in your revision. Remember: the real exam questions may not look like this.

1 (a) Which of the following is a test of flexibility? **(1)**

☐ **A** Standing stork test

☐ **B** Harvard step test

☐ **C** Sit and reach test

☐ **D** 30-metre sprint test

(b) There are many influences that can impact on an individual's choice of activity. Which category of the key influences do the following belong to: disability, age, race? **(1)**

☐ **A** People

☐ **B** Image

☐ **C** Cultural

☐ **D** Health and well-being

(c) Which **one** of the following would be the **most** important to a swimmer 600 metres into an 800-metre race? **(1)**

☐ **A** Muscular endurance

☐ **B** Muscular strength

☐ **C** Body composition

☐ **D** Flexibility

(d) Adopting a healthy active lifestyle can improve aspects of skill-related fitness. Which of the following is **not** an aspect of skill-related fitness? **(1)**

☐ **A** Agility

☐ **B** Speed

☐ **C** Reaction time

☐ **D** Cardiovascular fitness

(e)   Physical activity can improve your mental health. Which of the following is a mental benefit of taking part in physical activity?   **(1)**

☐   **A**   Improving performance

☐   **B**   Making new friends

☐   **C**   Working with others

☐   **D**   Increasing self-esteem

(f)   Which **one** of the following statements is **false**?   **(1)**

☐   **A**   Specificity means matching training to the requirements of an activity.

☐   **B**   Rest is the period of time allotted to recovery.

☐   **C**   Progressive overload means quickly increasing the amount of training so that it feels very hard.

☐   **D**   Reversibility can be caused by injury.

(g)   Calcium is vital to health, especially during childhood and adolescence. Which **one** of the following systems does it benefit **most**?   **(1)**

☐   **A**   Cardiovascular system

☐   **B**   Muscular system

☐   **C**   Skeletal system

☐   **D**   Respiratory system

(h)   Which **one** of the following statements correctly defines the term 'stroke volume'?   **(1)**

☐   **A**   The amount of blood ejected from the heart in one minute.

☐   **B**   The volume of blood pumped out of the heart by each ventricle during one contraction.

☐   **C**   The number of times the heart beats per minute.

☐   **D**   The force exerted by circulating blood on the walls of the blood vessels.

(i)   Which **one** of the following statements is **false**?   (1)

☐   **A**   The range of movement at the elbow is flexion and extension.

☐   **B**   The elbow and shoulder are both hinge joints.

☐   **C**   The shoulder joint can perform flexion, extension, adduction, abduction and rotation.

☐   **D**   Abduction is the movement away from the mid-line of the body.

(j)   A common injury, particularly in invasion games, is a sprained ankle. Which **one** of the following is **not** part of the RICE process to treat minor injuries?   (1)

☐   **A**   Rest

☐   **B**   Isolation

☐   **C**   Compression

☐   **D**   Elevation

(Total for Question 1 = 10 marks)

2 The individuals in **Figure 1** benefit from healthy active lifestyles.

Figure 1

Identify **two** social benefits of regular participation in physical activity. **(2)**

1 ....

2 ....

(Total for Question 2 = 2 marks)

3 Regular participation in physical activity is thought to be beneficial to the individual. Explain how participation in physical activity can stimulate:

Physical challenge **(3)**

....

....

....

....

....

....

(Total for Question 3 = 3 marks)

4 Thomas has just joined a local tennis centre just five minutes' walk from his house. He was inspired to take part in tennis after watching the Men's Olympic tennis final.

Which **two** different categories of key influences have impacted on Thomas' involvement in physical activity? **(2)**

1 ....

2 ....

(Total for Question 4 = 2 marks)

5 Identify **three different** components of skill-related fitness that would be relevant to all the performers in **Figure 2**.

Figure 2

Component 1 .... **(1)**

Component 2 .... **(1)**

Component 3 .... **(1)**

(Total for Question 5 = 3 marks)

6 (a) Describe the tests shown in **Figure 3** and give an example from a physical activity that would benefit from the results of each test.

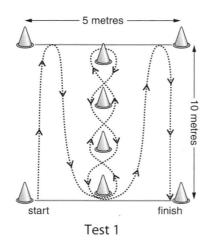

Test 1

Test 2

Figure 3

1 .... **(3)**

....

....

....

....

2 .... **(3)**

....

....

....

....

(b) Explain why a sprinter is unlikely to use the 12-minute Cooper run. **(3)**

....

....

....

....

....

....

(Total for Question 6 = 9 marks)

7   The performers in **Figure 4** have the same body type (somatotype).

Figure 4

(a)   Name the body type of the performers in **Figure 4**.   **(1)**

....

(b)   Describe a characteristic of this body type.   **(1)**

....

(c)   Give **two** different advantages of this body type, one for each performer below:

(i)   The sumo wrestler   **(1)**

....

(ii)   The rugby prop   **(1)**

....

Optimum weight varies for different athletic activities.

(d)   Explain the term 'optimum weight' and give an example of how optimum weight can affect performance.   **(3)**

....

....

....

....

....

(Total for Question 7 = 7 marks)

7

8   (a)   Diuretics are a category of performance-enhancing drugs. Name a sport where a performer might be tempted to take this drug and explain how it might be used to improve performance.   **(2)**

....

....

....

....

   (b)   State **two** negative effects of taking diuretics.   **(2)**

....

....

....

....

(Total for Question 8 = 4 marks)

9   Participating in activities like hockey, shown in **Figure 5**, involves risk.

Figure 5

Other than pulling a muscle, identify a **risk** that could be associated with this activity and a **measure** that could be used to reduce this risk.

Risk: **(1)**

....

Measure to reduce risk: **(1)**

....

....

(Total for Question 9 = 2 marks)

10   Mohammed plays football for the school team.

Mohammed is three weeks into his six-week personal exercise programme (PEP). In one circuit training session he measured his heart rate (HR): before he started the session, half an hour into his session and 15 minutes after his training session.

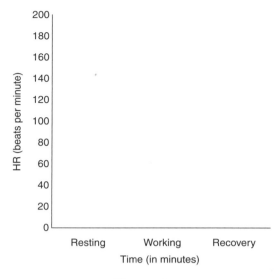

Figure 6

(a)   Plot on the graph where you think each of the following heart rate values should go: 77, 87, 189.   **(1)**

(b)   Explain why you chose the HR values in that order.   **(3)**

....

....

....

....

....

....

....

(c)   Explain why a professional marathon runner may have a lower resting heart rate than Mohammed.   **(2)**

....

....

....

....

(Total for Question 10 = 6 marks)

11 (a) Identify **two** long-term effects of regular participation in physical activity on the respiratory system. **(2)**

1 ....

2 ....

(b) Give an example of a performer who would benefit from **one** long-term effect identified in (a). **(1)**

....

(c) Explain why they would benefit from this. **(3)**

....

....

....

....

....

(Total for Question 11 = 6 marks)

12   **Figure 7** shows the knee joint. In the table:

(a)   State the **type** of joint at the knee.   **(1)**

(b)   State **one** range of movement at this joint.   **(1)**

(c)   Give **two** specific sporting examples where this range of movement is used at this joint.   **(2)**

	Type of joint	Range of movement at this joint	Specific sporting example where this range of movement is used at this joint
Figure 7			

(Total for Question 12 = 4 marks)

13 Nicola is a personal trainer. She is working with a group of boxers aiming to improve their health and fitness.

(a) Define the terms 'health' and 'fitness'. **(2)**

....

....

....

At the start of the six-week programme Nicola issued the boxers with a PAR-Q test.

(b) What is the purpose of a PAR-Q? **(1)**

....

....

(c) Nicola must consider SMART goals when planning the boxers' programme.

Explain how ensuring goals are realistic and time-bound can help Nicola plan an effective programme for the boxers. **(4)**

....

....

....

....

....

....

....

(d) Nicola believes that circuit training should be part of the boxers' training programme.

Describe how circuit training can be used to improve health and fitness. **(3)**

....

....

....

(Total for Question 13 = 10 marks)

14   Fred is a GCSE PE student. He is a keen hockey player.

Fred is starting to plan his personal exercise programme (PEP).

Discuss the use of the principles of training when planning a PEP.   **(6)**

....

....

....

....

....

....

....

....

....

....

....

....

....

....

....

....

....

....

....

(Total for Question 14 = 6 marks)

15 Diet can have an impact on the body systems.

Explain the impact of diet on the cardiovascular and skeletal systems. **(6)**

....

....

....

....

....

....

....

....

....

....

....

....

....

....

....

....

....

....

....

....

....

(Total for Question 15 = 6 marks)

TOTAL FOR PAPER = 80 MARKS

1 (a) Which **one** of the following statements correctly defines the term 'health'? **(1)**

☐ **A** The ability to meet the demands of the environment

☐ **B** Completing exercise on a regular basis

☐ **C** State of complete mental, physical and social well-being, not merely the absence of disease and infirmity

☐ **D** Feeling physically fit and well

(b) **Figure 1** shows the sports participation pyramid.

Which letter, **A**, **B**, **C** or **D**, represents the stage where participants regularly experience coaching in their specific sport? **(1)**

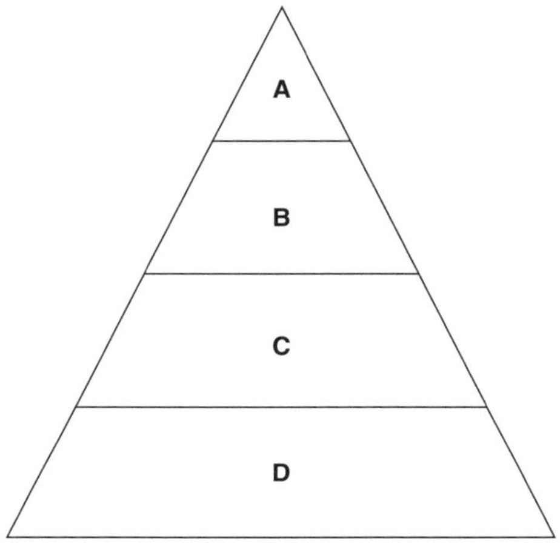

Figure 1

(c) Which **one** of the following performers would consider the endomorph somatotype to be the **most** appropriate body type for their activity? **(1)**

☐ **A** 800m runner

☐ **B** Shot putter

☐ **C** Long jumper

☐ **D** 100m runner

(d) Which **one** of the following is a short-term effect of participation in exercise on the respiratory system? **(1)**

☐ **A** Increased build-up of lactic acid

☐ **B** Increased breathing rate

☐ **C** Increased heart rate

☐ **D** Decreased vital capacity

(e)   Which **one** of the following is **not** an aspect of skill-related fitness?   **(1)**

☐   **A**   Agility

☐   **B**   Balance

☐   **C**   Flexibility

☐   **D**   Power

(f)   Which **one** of the following training methods would be **most** beneficial to a long-distance runner?   **(1)**

☐   **A**   Circuit

☐   **B**   Continuous

☐   **C**   Cross

☐   **D**   Weight

(g)   Despite the risks, some performers take drugs to improve their performance.

Which **one** of the following statements correctly links the performance-enhancing drug with its effect and a performer who would benefit from this effect?   **(1)**

☐   **A**   Peptide hormones taken by a snooker player to reduce anxiety levels

☐   **B**   Stimulants taken by a boxer to increase aggression

☐   **C**   Anabolic steroids taken by a boxer to speed up weight loss

☐   **D**   Narcotic analgesics taken by a cyclist to increase oxygen delivery during a long-distance event

(h)   Which **one** of the following muscles is contracting to allow the bowler in **Figure 2** to extend his arm at the elbow?   **(1)**

☐   **A**   Deltoid

☐   **B**   Biceps

☐   **C**   Triceps

☐   **D**   Pectorals

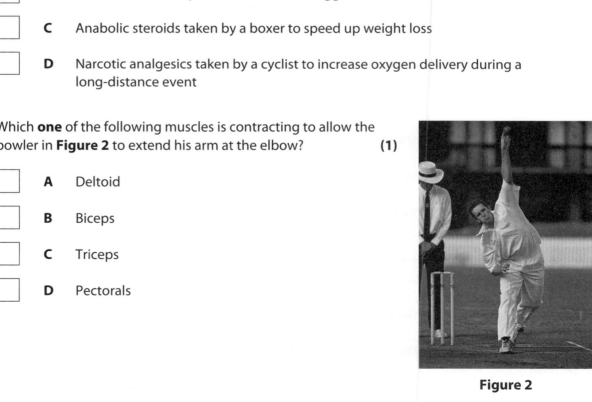

Figure 2

(i)   Muscular hypertrophy is one training adaptation that occurs as a result of long-term training.

Which **one** of the following methods of training is **most** likely to cause muscular
hypertrophy?   **(1)**

☐   **A**   Continuous

☐   **B**   Circuit

☐   **C**   Weight

☐   **D**   Cross

(j)   Sports performers injure themselves occasionally.

Which **one** of the following is **not** an example of a type of fracture?   **(1)**

☐   **A**   Greenstick

☐   **B**   Compound

☐   **C**   Stress

☐   **D**   Compress

(Total for Question 1 = 10 marks)

2   A sports centre is doing its annual data collection, aiming to find out which facilities are used most. The table below represents the data.

(a)   Complete the table, explaining how each activity could provide the stated classification of benefit.   **(4)**

Activity	How many people use it in a month	Main age range	Classification of benefit	Explanation of how stated benefit achieved
Swimming	436	25–30	Physical	
Netball	189	15–20	Social	

(b)   Brenda goes to the yoga class.

Describe how taking part in physical activity can make an individual feel good.   **(2)**

....

....

....

....

(c)   The sports centre is currently running a 'two for one' deal on classes. Brenda has decided to try out the aerobics class.

Identify which key influence may have led Brenda to take part.   **(1)**

....

(Total for Question 2 = 7 marks)

3 The required components of skill-related fitness vary for different activities.

In the table:

(a) Identify the **two** most important skill-related components for each performer. **(4)**

(b) State how your first chosen component for each performer is used in her activity. **(2)**

	Component choice one	Component choice two	How first-choice component for each performer is used in her activity
Gymnast			
Sprinter			

(Total for Question 3 = 6 marks)

4   Tom is a GCSE PE student. He is using interval training to improve his performance in sprinting.

(a)   State **two** characteristics of interval training.   **(2)**

....

....

(b)   Tom applies the principle of progressive overload to his training.

(i)   Describe the principle of 'progressive overload'.   **(1)**

....

....

....

(ii)   State why the principle of progressive overload should be applied.   **(1)**

....

(c)   If Tom stopped training, he might experience reversibility.

Explain the term 'reversibility' and how it could impact Tom's performance in sprinting.   **(3)**

....

....

....

....

(Total for Question 4 = 7 marks)

5   Amreet is a 30-year-old interested in improving her health and fitness.

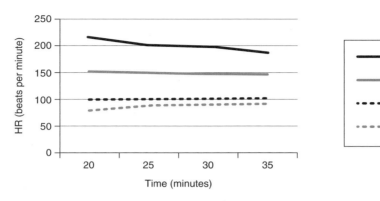

Figure 3

(a)   Which of the lines on the graph in **Figure 3** (**A**, **B**, **C** or **D**) would Amreet use to make sure
she was working within her target zone?   **(1)**

....

(b)   Explain your choice.   **(3)**

....

....

....

....

....

....

(Total for Question 5 = 4 marks)

6 (a) Explain the term 'anorexia'. (2)

....

....

....

(b) Explain **one** impact of being obese on achieving sustained involvement in physical activity. (3)

....

....

....

....

(Total for Question 6 = 5 marks)

7 Diet and rest need to be considered when planning a healthy active lifestyle.

Describe the impact of diet and rest on the muscular system.

(a) Impact of **diet** on the muscular system (2)

....

....

....

(b) Impact of **rest** on the muscular system (2)

....

....

....

(Total for Question 7 = 4 marks)

8   Although not illegal, alcohol and smoking do have dangerous side effects on the body.

Identify **two** possible health risks for each recreational drug in the table.   **(4)**

Recreational drug	Negative effect one	Negative effect two
Alcohol		
Smoking		

(Total for Question 8 = 4 marks)

9   Charlotte and Amit both compete in rugby.

Using an example, explain how balanced competition can reduce risk in physical activity.   **(3)**

....

....

....

....

(Total for Question 9 = 3 marks)

10   Increased stroke volume is a long-term effect of regular participation in physical activity on the cardiovascular system.

Describe **two** other long-term effects of regular participation in physical activity on the cardiovascular system.

Long-term effect 1   **(2)**

....

....

....

Long-term effect 2   **(2)**

....

....

....

(Total for Question 10 = 4 marks)

11   Oxygen debt is a short-term effect of participation in exercise.

(a)   Explain the term 'oxygen debt'.   **(3)**

....

....

....

....

(b)   For an activity of your choice, identify when the performer would experience oxygen debt in their activity.   **(1)**

Name of activity ....

....

(Total for Question 11 = 4 marks)

12   **Figure 4** shows an athlete clearing a hurdle.

Figure 4

Complete the statements below by identifying which muscles are contracting to allow the hurdler to achieve the described actions.

(a)   Straightening the leg over the hurdle   **(1)**

....

(b)   Bending the trailing leg going over the hurdle   **(1)**

....

(Total for Question 12 = 2 marks)

13   The skeletal system has several functions.

(a)   Using an example from sport, describe how the skeleton gives protection.   **(3)**

....

....

....

The skeleton also aids movement.

(b)   Identify the range of movement at the following joints.

(i)   Shoulder   **(1)**

....

(ii)   Knee   **(1)**

....

(c)   (i)   Identify **one** effect of regular participation in physical activity on the skeletal system.   **(1)**

....

(ii)   For a named sport, state **one** way in which the effect you have identified in (c) (i) can benefit the performer.   **(1)**

....

....

....

(d)   Bones become lighter and lose density with age. Give an example of how performers can delay the onset of osteoporosis.   **(1)**

....

....

(Total for Question 13 = 8 marks)

14 Using examples of relevant agencies, discuss the common purposes of initiatives developed to provide opportunities for becoming or remaining involved in physical activity. **(6)**

....

....

....

....

....

....

....

....

....

....

....

....

....

....

....

....

....

....

....

....

....

....

(Total for Question 14 = 6 marks)

15   Some sports performers choose to take performance-enhancing drugs although these are illegal.

Discuss the use of erythropoietin / EPO for enhancing performance.   **(6)**

....

....

....

....

....

....

....

....

....

....

....

....

....

....

....

....

....

....

....

....

(Total for Question 15 = 6 marks)

TOTAL FOR PAPER = 80 MARKS

1 (a) Which **one** of the following is an example of a 'resources' key influence that can impact on achieving sustained involvement in physical activity? **(1)**

☐ **A** Role models

☐ **B** Fashion

☐ **C** Location

☐ **D** Disability

(b) Initiatives such as Sport England aim to contribute to the development of healthy lifestyles. Which of the following is **not** an aim of initiatives? **(1)**

☐ **A** Retain people in physical activity

☐ **B** Create opportunities for participation

☐ **C** Increase participation in physical activity

☐ **D** Increase earning potential of elite athletes

(c) Which of the following is the correct definition of muscular endurance? **(1)**

☐ **A** The amount of force a muscle can exert against a resistance

☐ **B** The ability to use voluntary muscles many times without getting tired

☐ **C** The ability to exercise the entire body for long periods of time without tiring

☐ **D** The ability to do strength performances quickly

(d) Which of the following is **not** a test of cardiovascular fitness? **(1)**

☐ **A** Treadmill test

☐ **B** Harvard step test

☐ **C** 30-metre sprint

☐ **D** Cooper's 12-minute run test

(e)   Which of the performers in the following statements is applying the principle of specificity?   **(1)**

   □   **A**   A tennis player practising their first serves

   □   **B**   A track sprinter doing interval training in the swimming pool

   □   **C**   A shot putter taking part in continuous training

   □   **D**   A basketball player working on their speed at the track

(f)   Which of the following statements correctly describes blood flow during exercise?   **(1)**

   □   **A**   Blood flow to the digestive system is lower at rest than when exercising.

   □   **B**   Blood flow is distributed equally between the muscular system and the digestive system at rest and when exercising.

   □   **C**   Blood flow to the digestive system is greater at rest than when exercising.

   □   **D**   Blood flow to the muscular system is lower during exercise than at rest.

(g)   Which of the following is **not** a factor that can affect optimum weight?   **(1)**

   □   **A**   Height

   □   **B**   Gender

   □   **C**   Muscle girth

   □   **D**   Consumption of fat in diet

(h)   **Figure 1** shows a long-distance runner's heart rate during a 10-kilometre race.

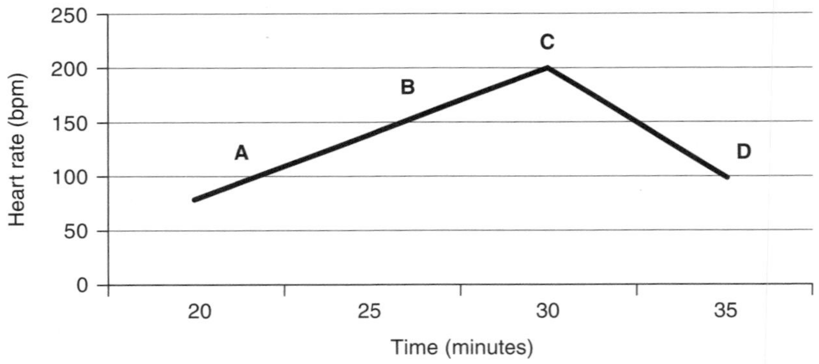

Figure 1

Using **Figure 1**, at which point, **A**, **B**, **C** or **D**, does the performer begin to apply the principle of rest and recovery?   **(1)**

   □   **A**   □   **B**   □   **C**   □   **D**

(i)   Which of the following is a short-term effect of exercise on the muscular system?   **(1)**

      ☐   **A**   Increased breathing rate

      ☐   **B**   Increased production of lactic acid

      ☐   **C**   Muscular hypertrophy

      ☐   **D**   Increased strength of ligaments and tendons

(j)   **Figure 2** shows a performer on the trampoline performing the pike jump.

Figure 2

Which of the following muscles flexes the trunk to create the pike position?   **(1)**

      ☐   **A**   Latissimus dorsi

      ☐   **B**   Trapezius

      ☐   **C**   Deltoid

      ☐   **D**   Abdominals

(Total for Question 1 = 10 marks)

2   **Figure 3** shows the sports participation pyramid.

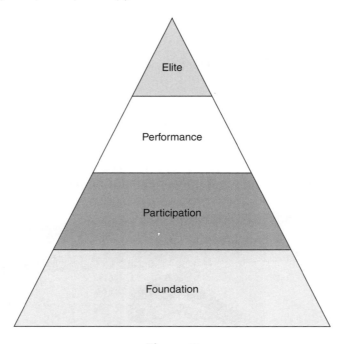

Figure 3

(a)   Explain why the elite stage of the sports participation pyramid has the **smallest** number of participants.

(3)

....

....

....

....

....

....

(b)   Describe how physical activity allows people to remain involved in sport when they are no longer able to be a performer.

(2)

....

....

(Total for Question 2 = 5 marks)

3   Complete the table below by giving an example of how flexibility would be used by each performer.

(3)

Performer	How flexibility is used in their activity
Hurdler	
Gymnast	
Tennis player	

(Total for Question 3 = 3 marks)

4 Mrs Sharma is a PE teacher. She is concerned about the health of some of the sixth form students. She has decided to set up a lunchtime badminton club. Mrs Sharma gives all pupils a physical activity readiness questionnaire (PAR-Q) at the start of the term.

(a) Give an example of a 'typical' question that might be asked on a PAR-Q. **(1)**

....

....

....

....

(b) Mrs Sharma believes that the sixth form students' health will be improved by taking part in exercise.

Explain the term 'health'. **(2)**

....

....

....

....

....

(c) Before each badminton game Mrs Sharma leads a warm-up.

Explain the purpose of a 'warm-up'. **(3)**

....

....

....

....

....

(Total for Question 4 = 6 marks)

5 When setting goals to plan involvement in physical activity, it is important to apply the principles of SMART targets.

(a) Explain why it is important that each target is 'specific'. **(2)**

....

....

....

....

(b) Give **one** example of a 'measurable' goal. **(1)**

....

....

(Total for Question 5 = 3 marks)

6 (a) Explain the importance of macronutrients in maintaining a healthy active lifestyle. **(3)**

....

....

....

....

....

(b) Explain why it is important to consider the timing of dietary intake when performing exercise. **(2)**

....

....

....

....

....

(Total for Question 6 = 5 marks)

7 Despite the risks, some performers take drugs to enhance their performance.

In the table:

(a) Identify **one** possible health risk of taking each performance-enhancing drug. **(3)**

Performance-enhancing drug	Health risk	
Diuretics		
Anabolic steroids		
Narcotic analgesics		

(b) Using an example, explain why a performer might risk using beta blockers to enhance performance. **(3)**

....

....

....

....

(Total for Question 7 = 6 marks)

8   **Figure 4** shows Will during a continuous training session in preparation for his next marathon.

Figure 4

(a)   Explain why Will would choose this method of training.   **(2)**

....

....

....

(b)   State whether continuous training is aerobic or anaerobic.   **(1)**

....

(c)   Describe how Will could apply **two** of the components of the FITT training principle to his continuous training.   **(4)**

....

....

....

....

....

....

....

....

(Total for Question 8 = 7 marks)

9   Shania plays hockey for the school team. It is important she wears shin pads to prevent injury.

State **two** other ways that Shania could avoid injury.   **(2)**

1 ....

2 ....

(Total for Question 9 = 2 marks)

10 Jai is a keen volleyball player. During a match his blood pressure and heart rate increase.

  (a) Explain why the cardiovascular system responds in this way when beginning exercise. **(4)**

  Heart rate increases because

  ....

  ....

  Blood pressure increases because

  ....

  ....

  ....

  (b) Jai ensures he has a day off training after a match.

  Explain the impact of rest on Jai's cardiovascular system. **(2)**

  ....

  ....

  ....

(Total for Question 10 = 6 marks)

11 Describe the impact of smoking on a long-distance runner's performance. **(2)**

....

....

....

....

(Total for Question 11 = 2 marks)

12   Sameleh takes part in the school sports day in three events. He has been observing elite athletes in each of his events.

Identify which muscles are contracting to achieve the actions in **Figure 5**.   (3)

Keeping the arm straight at the elbow in the shot put

....

Keeping the leg straight at the knee in the pole vault

....

Moving the arm away from the mid-line of the body in the discus

....

Figure 5

(Total for Question 12 = 3 marks)

13 The skeletal system plays an important role in allowing for a healthy active lifestyle. **Figure 6** shows the skeletal system of a football player preparing to kick the ball.

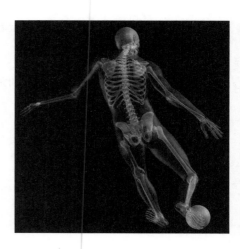

Figure 6

(a) Identify **three** functions of the skeletal system in use during physical activity. **(3)**

1 ....

2 ....

3 ....

(b) Give **one** example of how each function is used during a football game. **(3)**

1 ....

2 ....

3 ....

....

(Total for Question 13 = 6 marks)

14 Describe **two** named types of fracture. **(4)**

1 ....

....

2 ....

....

(Total for Question 14 = 4 marks)

15 Using examples, explain how taking part in physical activity can stimulate cooperation and
physical challenge.   **(6)**

....

....

....

....

....

....

....

....

....

....

....

....

....

....

....

....

....

....

....

....

....

....

(Total for Question 15 = 6 marks)

16   Paul is a long-distance runner and Alana is a sprinter. They are both sixteen years old.

Explain how they would use heart rate target zones within their training.   **(6)**

....

....

....

....

....

....

....

....

....

....

....

....

....

....

....

....

....

....

....

....

....

....

(Total for Question 16 = 6 marks)

TOTAL FOR PAPER = 80 MARKS

1 (a) Which of the following **best** describes a healthy active lifestyle? **(1)**

   ☐ **A**   Eating a healthy balanced diet and walking 20 minutes every day

   ☐ **B**   Playing in a badminton match

   ☐ **C**   Playing for a local hockey team and training twice a week

   ☐ **D**   Going to aerobics twice a week with friends

(b) Which **one** of the following is **not** a mental benefit of taking part in physical activity? **(1)**

   ☐ **A**   Feeling good

   ☐ **B**   Cooperation

   ☐ **C**   Aesthetic appreciation

   ☐ **D**   Physical challenge

(c) The following statements were made by students explaining what influenced them when deciding whether or not to participate in an activity. Which of the statements relate to the category of key influence 'people'? **(1)**

   ☐ **A**   Whether the activity is within walking distance of your house

   ☐ **B**   Whether you have a long-term illness

   ☐ **C**   Whether it has been shown on television

   ☐ **D**   Whether your friends like the activity

(d) Which of the following correctly defines 'exercise'? **(1)**

   ☐ **A**   The ability to meet the demands of the environment

   ☐ **B**   To gradually increase the amount of overload so that fitness gains occur, without potential for injury

   ☐ **C**   A form of physical activity done to maintain or improve health and physical fitness. It is not competitive sport.

   ☐ **D**   Playing sport against another team

(e)   Which of the following correctly defines 'recovery'?   **(1)**

☐   **A**   The period of time allotted to recovery

☐   **B**   The time required for the repair of damage to the body caused by training or competition

☐   **C**   Any adaptation that takes place as a consequence of training, which will be reversed when you stop training

☐   **D**   The time taken over a six-week training period to ensure training goals are met

(f)   Which of the following statements is a benefit of a cool-down?   **(1)**

☐   **A**   It aids the removal of lactic acid

☐   **B**   It slowly increases the heart rate and breathing rate

☐   **C**   It decreases flexibility

☐   **D**   It reduces the chance of injury during the activity

(g)   Which of the following performers would consider an ectomorph somatotype to be the most appropriate body type for their activity?   **(1)**

☐   **A**   100m sprinter

☐   **B**   Hammer thrower

☐   **C**   High jumper

☐   **D**   Shot putter

(h)   If an individual had high levels of low density lipoprotein (LDL, 'bad cholesterol'), which of the following should he or she avoid in order to improve his / her health?   **(1)**

☐   **A**   Gentle exercise

☐   **B**   Foods high in saturated fat

☐   **C**   Moderate exercise

☐   **D**   Foods high in unsaturated fat (e.g. sunflower oil, nuts)

(i)   Which **one** of the following is an effect of smoking on the respiratory system?   **(1)**

☐   **A**   Increased lung capacity

☐   **B**   Oxygen debt

☐   **C**   Increased breathing rate

☐   **D**   Reduction in oxygen uptake by red blood cells

(j)   Which of the following joint actions would occur as a result of the biceps contracting?   **(1)**

☐   **A**   Flexion

☐   **B**   Extension

☐   **C**   Adduction

☐   **D**   Abduction

(Total for Question 1 = 10 marks)

2   Peggy and Joan play badminton weekly as part of a healthy active lifestyle.

Figure 1 below shows Peggy and Joan deciding service before their badminton match.

Figure 1

Apart from the possible mental benefits, why else would over-50s badminton players take part in physical activity?   (2)

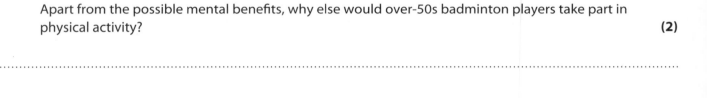

(Total for Question 2 = 2 marks)

3   **Figure 2** shows the sports participation pyramid.

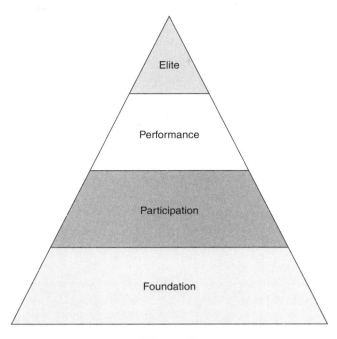

Figure 2

(a)   Explain the participation stage of the pyramid.   **(3)**

....

....

....

....

....

(b)   Outline how someone can move from the participation to the performance stage of the
       sports participation pyramid.   **(2)**

....

....

(Total for Question 3 = 5 marks)

4   Health-related exercise demands can vary within sporting activities.

Using an example, explain the importance of body composition to a performer in their activity.   **(3)**

....

....

....

....

....

....

....

....

(Total for Question 4 = 3 marks)

5   The Stratford family are very keen on taking part in sport. The father, Mike, is 36 and is a keen
rugby player who plays regularly on Saturdays for the local team. Darcey, his daughter, is 16. She
has just reached the regional under-16 tennis final.

(a)   Explain why it is important for Mike and Darcey to consider individual differences when
developing their weight training programme.   **(2)**

....

....

....

....

....

....

(b)   Describe how Mike and Darcey could use each aspect of the FITT principle to improve their
fitness and level of performance when participating in their activities.   **(4)**

....

....

....

....

....

....

....

....

....

....

....

....

(Total for Question 5 = 6 marks)

6 State **three** reasons why performers use goal setting. **(3)**

1 ....

....

2 ....

....

3 ....

....

(Total for Question 6 = 3 marks)

7 (a) Identify **three different** training methods that could be adapted for use by a performer who needs high levels of power for their activity. **(3)**

1 ....

2 ....

3 ....

(b) Describe how **one** of the methods you identified in (a) could be used to improve power. **(3)**

....

....

....

....

(Total for Question 7 = 6 marks)

8   (a)   Explain how **two** requirements of a balanced diet can aid physical activity.   **(3)**

....

....

....

....

....

....

(b)   Explain why it is important to consider the timing of your dietary intake before taking part in physical activity.   **(2)**

....

....

....

....

....

....

....

....

(Total for Question 8 = 5 marks)

9   (a)   Define the term 'anorexia'.   **(1)**

....

(b)   State how any **two** symptoms of anorexia would impact on achieving sustained involvement in physical activity.   **(2)**

1 ....

....

2 ....

....

(Total for Question 9 = 3 marks)

10   Complete the following table by:

Identifying a risk reduction measure relevant to the activity in **Figures 3**, **4** and **5**   (3)

Stating how the identified risk reduction measure reduces risk associated with the activity   (3)

Activity where used	Risk reduction measure relevant to the activity	How risk is reduced through this measure
Figure 3		
Figure 4		
Figure 5		

(Total for Question 10 = 6 marks)

11 (a) The equation below is incomplete.

Complete the equation that is used to calculate the amount of blood ejected from the heart per minute. **(1)**

.... = ... × stroke volume

(b) A healthy active lifestyle will have an impact on the body systems. Explain **two** short-term effects of exercise on the body's cardiovascular system. **(4)**

1 ....

....

....

2 ....

....

....

(Total for Question 11 = 5 marks)

12 Regular participation in exercise can have long-term effects on the body systems. One long-term effect of regular exercise on the respiratory system is an increased number of alveoli.

Describe the benefits of this adaptation. **(2)**

....

....

....

....

....

(Total for Question 12 = 2 marks)

13 (a) Complete the table below. **(4)**

Name of contraction	Definition of contraction	Sporting example
Isotonic contraction		
Isometric contraction		

(b) Describe the execution of a technique in an activity of your choice that is brought about by the contraction of the hamstrings. **(2)**

....

....

(Total for Question 13 = 6 marks)

14 (a) Give an example of a ball and socket joint. **(1)**

....

(b) State the range of movement possible at a ball and socket joint. **(1)**

....

(c) Give a specific sporting action where this range of movement is used at this joint. **(1)**

....

(Total for Question 14 = 3 marks)

15 Weight-bearing activities can increase the strength of ligaments and tendons.

Using an example, explain why stronger ligaments and tendons will be beneficial to a performer of your choice. **(3)**

....

....

....

....

(Total for Question 15 = 3 marks)

16 Discuss the use of coordination by each performer in **Figures 6**, **7** and **8**. (6)

Figure 6   **Figure 7**   **Figure 8**

....

....

....

....

....

....

....

....

....

....

....

....

....

....

....

....

(Total for Question 16 = 6 marks)

17   Shuti exercises regularly to increase her fitness.

Explain the short- and long-term effects and benefits of regular exercise on the muscular system and future performance.

(6)

....

....

....

....

....

....

....

....

....

....

....

....

....

....

....

....

....

....

....

....

(Total for Question 17 = 6 marks)

TOTAL FOR PAPER = 80 MARKS

1   Which **one** of the following statements describes a physical benefit of exercise?   **(1)**

   ☐   **A**   Increase in serotonin

   ☐   **B**   Increase in self-esteem

   ☐   **C**   Losing weight if overweight

   ☐   **D**   Improving cooperation skills

(Total for Question 1 = 1 mark)

2   Which of the following is **not** an example of a 'resources' key influence?   **(1)**

   ☐   **A**   Location

   ☐   **B**   Access

   ☐   **C**   Cost

   ☐   **D**   Time

(Total for Question 2 = 1 mark)

3   Which of the following is an essential macronutrient in a healthy diet?   **(1)**

   ☐   **A**   Protein

   ☐   **B**   Water

   ☐   **C**   Fibre

   ☐   **D**   Vitamins

(Total for Question 3 = 1 mark)

4   Olivia goes to the after-school rounders and netball club.

   Which stage of the sports participation pyramid would she be considered to have reached?   **(1)**

   ☐   **A**   Foundation

   ☐   **B**   Performance

   ☐   **C**   Participation

   ☐   **D**   Elite

(Total for Question 4 = 1 mark)

5 Which of the following is a correct statement about flexibility? (1)

- [ ] **A** It is the ability to change the position of the body quickly

- [ ] **B** It is the ability to use two or more body parts together

- [ ] **C** It is the ability to retain the body's centre of mass over the base of support

- [ ] **D** It is the range of movement at a joint

(Total for Question 5 = 1 mark)

6 **Figure 1** shows a 200m butterfly swimmer.

Figure 1

Which of the following components of health-related exercise is **most** important for this performer in the last 25m of a race? (1)

- [ ] **A** Muscular strength

- [ ] **B** Body composition

- [ ] **C** Flexibility

- [ ] **D** Muscular endurance

(Total for Question 6 = 1 mark)

7 Which of the following components of skill-related fitness does the standing three-ball juggle measure? (1)

- [ ] **A** Speed

- [ ] **B** Coordination

- [ ] **C** Balance

- [ ] **D** Reaction time

(Total for Question 7 = 1 mark)

8 Which **one** of the following is a correct statement relating to the Harvard step test? **(1)**

☐ **A** It is used to measure muscular strength

☐ **B** The result is based on heart rate readings

☐ **C** It is used to test anaerobic fitness

☐ **D** The equipment required to carry out the test is a treadmill

(Total for Question 8 = 1 mark)

9 As part of a healthy active lifestyle, an individual should apply the principles of training in their personal exercise programme. Which of the following training methods is a shot putter likely to use if they are applying the principle of specificity to their training programme? **(1)**

☐ **A** Continuous training

☐ **B** Circuit training

☐ **C** Weight training

☐ **D** Interval training

(Total for Question 9 = 1 mark)

10 Which of the following is a correct description of 'progressive overload'? **(1)**

☐ **A** Matching training to the particular requirements of an activity

☐ **B** Making sure there is enough time between training sessions so that adaptation can take place

☐ **C** Increasing the intensity too much, causing injury to the muscle

☐ **D** Increasing intensity a little more each week once your body has adapted to the previous workload

(Total for Question 10 = 1 mark)

11 Which of the following is a form of interval training? **(1)**

☐ **A** Running for 30 minutes without a break

☐ **B** Holding a weight for 10 seconds, having a break and then holding the weight for another 10 seconds

☐ **C** Run 100 metres, rest for 1 minute and do this for 10 reps

☐ **D** Cycling 10 miles

(Total for Question 11 = 1 mark)

12 Which of the following is a correct statement relating to goal setting? **(1)**

☐ **A** Goal setting can increase motivation.

☐ **B** Goal setting can increase cooperation.

☐ **C** Goal setting can increase competition.

☐ **D** Goal setting can decrease reversibility.

(Total for Question 12 = 1 mark)

13 Which of the following is a measurable goal? **(1)**

☐ **A** To score more goals in netball

☐ **B** To be more accurate in shooting

☐ **C** To run 5k 2 seconds faster

☐ **D** To beat my rival in sprinting

(Total for Question 13 = 1 mark)

14 Which of the following is represented by the **R** in SMART goal setting? **(1)**

☐ **A** Reversibility

☐ **B** Realistic

☐ **C** Rest

☐ **D** Regular

(Total for Question 14 = 1 mark)

15 Which of the following should form the **smallest** percentage of macronutrients in the diet? **(1)**

☐ **A** Protein

☐ **B** Fats

☐ **C** Carbohydrates

☐ **D** Fibre

(Total for Question 15 = 1 mark)

16   Which percentage of their training threshold would a performer be working at if they wanted to improve anaerobic endurance?   (1)

☐   **A**   60–80%

☐   **B**   50–60%

☐   **C**   80–90%

☐   **D**   90–100%

(Total for Question 16 = 1 mark)

17   Explain how participation in physical activity can stimulate the development of friendships.   (2)

....

....

....

(Total for Question 17 = 2 marks)

18   Give an example of the key influence 'image'.   (1)

....

(Total for Question 18 = 1 mark)

19   Brian has played tennis for 15 years but has injured his knee and cannot take part as a performer any longer. Explain how he could stay involved in tennis.   (3)

....

....

....

....

(Total for Question 19 = 3 marks)

20 Stanley has started attending exercise to music classes to improve his fitness.

Explain the relationship between exercise and fitness. **(3)**

....

....

....

(Total for Question 20 = 3 marks)

21 **Figures 2** and **3** show performers using balance.

Complete the table by explaining how balance would be used by each performer. **(4)**

Performer	How they use balance
Figure 2 Horse riding	
Figure 3 Hammer throwing	

(Total for Question 21 = 4 marks)

22   Anisha throws the shot. She would like to increase her muscular strength to improve her performance. She is following a personal exercise programme.

Explain how Anisha could use the FITT principle to improve her muscular strength.   **(3)**

....

....

....

....

....

(Total for Question 22 = 3 marks)

23   Describe the role of carbohydrates in a healthy balanced diet.   **(2)**

....

....

....

....

(Total for Question 23 = 2 marks)

24 Donna is coaching the under-16 football team and is planning to use fartlek training as a method of training. Evaluate whether fartlek training would be the most appropriate choice of training for all members of the football team. **(6)**

....

....

....

....

....

....

....

....

....

....

....

....

....

....

....

....

....

....

....

....

....

....

(Total for Question 24 = 6 marks)

TOTAL FOR PAPER = 80 MARKS

1   Which of the following is **not** a physical benefit of exercise?   **(1)**

    ☐   **A**   Improved fitness

    ☐   **B**   Improved self-esteem

    ☐   **C**   Improved muscular endurance

    ☐   **D**   Increased strength

                                                                                    (Total for Question 1 = 1 mark)

2   Which of the following benefits is **most** likely to occur from taking part in team sports compared
    to individual sports?   **(1)**

    ☐   **A**   Increased competition

    ☐   **B**   Aesthetic appreciation

    ☐   **C**   Physical challenge

    ☐   **D**   Improved cooperation

                                                                                    (Total for Question 2 = 1 mark)

Questions 3 and 4 relate to the key influences that impact on participation.

3   Which of the following is an example of the participation key influence 'culture'?   **(1)**

    ☐   **A**   Peers

    ☐   **B**   Family

    ☐   **C**   Status

    ☐   **D**   Disability

                                                                                    (Total for Question 3 = 1 mark)

4   Which of the following describes a socioeconomic influence for taking part in exercise?   **(1)**

    ☐   **A**   I joined the local orienteering group as they meet near my house.

    ☐   **B**   I play golf at a private golf club as it is important how people see me and my business.

    ☐   **C**   I cycle because I want to be as well known as Sir Bradley Wiggins.

    ☐   **D**   I have taken up hurdling because I saw it on the television.

                                                                                    (Total for Question 4 = 1 mark)

5 Niqa used to play football regularly, but due to an injury he now watches his children play instead. He knows a lot about the game and wants to get involved but is only available on match days. Which of the following roles could Niqa adopt? **(1)**

☐ **A** Coach

☐ **B** Volunteer

☐ **C** Referee

☐ **D** Performer

(Total for Question 5 = 1 mark)

6 Which of the following defines the term 'fitness'? **(1)**

☐ **A** The ability to meet the demands of the environment

☐ **B** A form of physical activity done to maintain or improve health and/or physical fitness

☐ **C** A state of complete mental, physical and social well-being, not merely the absence of disease or infirmity

☐ **D** Any form of exercise or movement

(Total for Question 6 = 1 mark)

7 Which of the statements below accurately describes when the performer would use cardiovascular endurance in their activity? **(1)**

☐ **A** A goalkeeper in the 81st minute of the match running off her line to make a save

☐ **B** A rower at the start of the race

☐ **C** A 100m sprinter towards the end of his race

☐ **D** A tennis player during a long hard rally in the fifth set

(Total for Question 7 = 1 mark)

8 Which of the following is the **most** appropriate method of training for a performer wishing to improve their cardiovascular endurance? **(1)**

☐ **A** Interval

☐ **B** Weight

☐ **C** Continuous

☐ **D** Cross

(Total for Question 8 = 1 mark)

9 Which of the following is **not** a component of the FITT principle? **(1)**

☐ **A** Frequency

☐ **B** Time

☐ **C** Type

☐ **D** Target zone

(Total for Question 9 = 1 mark)

10 Alana is a pentathlete, so she has to train to improve performance in fencing, swimming, shooting, running and show jumping. Which of the methods of training would be **most** suitable for her? **(1)**

☐ **A** Interval training

☐ **B** Continuous training

☐ **C** Cross training

☐ **D** Weight training

(Total for Question 10 = 1 mark)

11 Which fitness test protocol is being described below? **(1)**

Stand side on to a wall, feet flat on the floor. Mark the highest point where the tips of your fingers can reach the wall. Jump as high as you can.

☐ **A** Harvard step test

☐ **B** Standing broad jump

☐ **C** Sargent jump test

☐ **D** Standing stork test

(Total for Question 11 = 1 mark)

12 Which **one** of the following is a correct statement relating to the three-ball juggling test? **(1)**

☐ **A** Stand 3 metres away from the wall

☐ **B** It is a test of reaction time

☐ **C** Another person counts how many catches you complete

☐ **D** You can catch the ball with both hands

(Total for Question 12 = 1 mark)

13 Which of the following is a benefit of a warm-up? **(1)**

☐ **A** Focuses your mind

☐ **B** Increases lactic acid production

☐ **C** Reduces the chance of injury after the activity

☐ **D** Decreases blood flow to the muscles before exercise

(Total for Question 13 = 1 mark)

14 The graph in **Figure 1** shows suggested target heart rate zones depending on age.

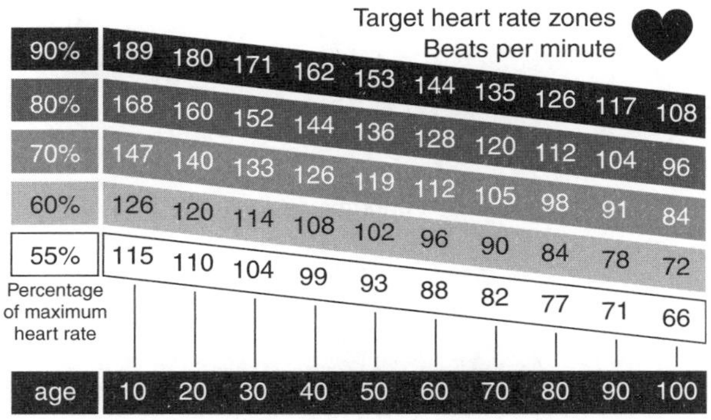

Figure 1

Using the information in **Figure 1**, which of the following is the most likely target heart rate zone for a healthy 20-year-old who wishes to improve their anaerobic fitness? **(1)**

☐ **A** 200–220 bpm

☐ **B** 140–160 bpm

☐ **C** 160–180 bpm

☐ **D** 110–180 bpm

(Total for Question 14 = 1 mark)

15 Planning what and when you eat is an important part of leading a healthy active lifestyle. Which of the following would be the **most** appropriate amount of time to leave before exercising after a large meal? **(1)**

☐ **A** Five minutes

☐ **B** Half an hour

☐ **C** 45 minutes

☐ **D** Over an hour

(Total for Question 15 = 1 mark)

16 Which of the following nutrients provides energy for **both** anaerobic and aerobic activity? (1)

A Fats

B Protein

C Carbohydrates

D Vitamins

(Total for Question 16 = 1 mark)

17 **Figure 2** shows the sports participation pyramid.

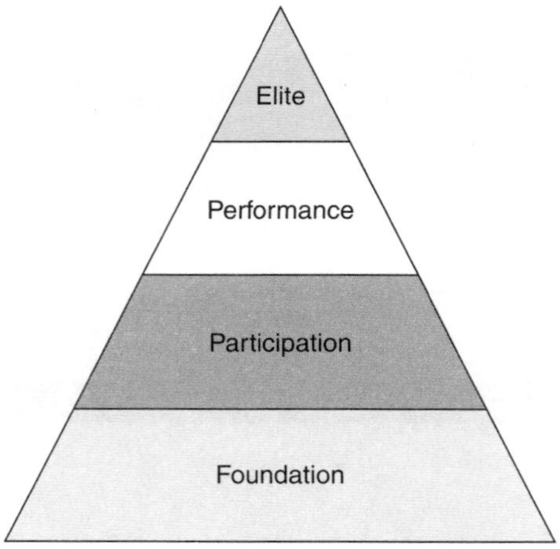

Figure 2

Using an example, describe the foundation stage of the pyramid. (3)

....

....

....

....

(Total for Question 17 = 3 marks)

18 There are many initiatives to increase participation in sport. Describe **one** other common purpose of initiatives. **(2)**

....

....

....

....

(Total for Question 18 = 2 marks)

19 Goal setting is used to improve performance. Explain **one** reason why it is important that set goals are specific. **(3)**

....

....

....

....

....

(Total for Question 19 = 3 marks)

20 Explain the term 'reversibility'. **(3)**

....

....

....

....

....

(Total for Question 20 = 3 marks)

21 Using an example, describe the purpose of a cool-down in an exercise session. **(3)**

....

....

....

....

....

....

(Total for Question 21 = 3 marks)

22 **(a)** Joel is a 100m sprinter. Before he begins his training he completes a number of fitness tests. Explain why the Illinois Agility Test would not be an appropriate test for Joel to undertake. **(2)**

....

....

....

....

....

(b) Explain a suitable test for Joel. **(2)**

....

....

....

....

....

(Total for Question 22 = 4 marks)

23   Evaluate the importance of body composition for a boxer and a ~~long~~ high jumper, giving examples of
      its possible effect on performance.   **(6)**

....

....

....

....

....

....

....

....

....

....

....

....

....

....

....

....

....

....

....

....

....

....

....

....

(Total for Question 23 = 6 marks)

TOTAL FOR PAPER = 40 MARKS)

1 (a) Which of the following is a test of flexibility? (1)

- [ ] **A** Standing stork test
- [ ] **B** Harvard step test
- [X] **C** Sit and reach test ✓
- [ ] **D** 30-metre sprint test

(b) There are many influences that can impact on an individual's choice of activity. Which category of the key influences do the following belong to: disability, age, race? (1)

- [ ] **A** People
- [ ] **B** Image
- [X] **C** Cultural ✓
- [ ] **D** Health and well-being

(c) Which **one** of the following would be the **most** important to a swimmer 600 metres into an 800-metre race? (1)

- [X] **A** Muscular endurance ✓
- [ ] **B** Muscular strength
- [ ] **C** Body composition
- [ ] **D** Flexibility

(d) Adopting a healthy active lifestyle can improve aspects of skill-related fitness. Which of the following is **not** an aspect of skill-related fitness? (1)

- [ ] **A** Agility
- [ ] **B** Speed
- [ ] **C** Reaction time
- [X] **D** Cardiovascular fitness ✓

(e) Physical activity can improve your mental health. Which of the following is a mental benefit of taking part in physical activity? (1)

- [ ] **A** Improving performance
- [ ] **B** Making new friends
- [ ] **C** Working with others
- [X] **D** Increasing self-esteem ✓

(f) Which **one** of the following statements is **false**? (1)

- [ ] **A** Specificity means matching training to the requirements of an activity.
- [ ] **B** Rest is the period of time allotted to recovery.
- [X] **C** Progressive overload means quickly increasing the amount of training so that it feels very hard. ✓
- [ ] **D** Reversibility can be caused by injury.

(g) Calcium is vital to health, especially during childhood and adolescence. Which **one** of the following systems does it benefit **most**? (1)

- [ ] **A** Cardiovascular system
- [ ] **B** Muscular system
- [X] **C** Skeletal system ✓
- [ ] **D** Respiratory system

(h) Which **one** of the following statements correctly defines the term 'stroke volume'? (1)

- [ ] **A** The amount of blood ejected from the heart in one minute.
- [X] **B** The volume of blood pumped out of the heart by each ventricle during one contraction. ✓
- [ ] **C** The number of times the heart beats per minute.
- [ ] **D** The force exerted by circulating blood on the walls of the blood vessels.

(i) Which **one** of the following statements is **false**? (1)

- [ ] **A** The range of movement at the elbow is flexion and extension.
- [X] **B** The elbow and shoulder are both hinge joints. ✓
- [ ] **C** The shoulder joint can perform flexion, extension, adduction, abduction and rotation.
- [ ] **D** Abduction is the movement away from the mid-line of the body.

(j) A common injury, particularly in invasion games, is a sprained ankle. Which **one** of the following is **not** part of the RICE process to treat minor injuries? (1)

- [ ] **A** Rest
- [X] **B** Isolation ✓
- [ ] **C** Compression
- [ ] **D** Elevation

(Total for Question 1 = 10 marks)

2 The individuals in **Figure 1** benefit from healthy active lifestyles.

Figure 1

Identify **two** social benefits of regular participation in physical activity. (2)

1 Make new friends ✓

2 Develop teamwork ✓

> You could also have written 'develop cooperation' / 'working with others' as a social benefit.

(Total for Question 2 = 2 marks)

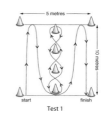

3 Regular participation in physical activity is thought to be beneficial to the individual. Explain how participation in physical activity can stimulate:

Physical challenge

> Ensure you consider the importance of 'the challenge'; no credit will be given for explanation in terms of 'normal training'.

Working your body to the limit physically ✓ and mentally and not giving up ✓ until you achieve your challenge, for example taking part in the London Marathon. ✓

(Total for Question 3 = 3 marks)

4 Thomas has just joined a local tennis centre just five minutes' walk from his house. He was inspired to take part in tennis after watching the Men's Olympic tennis final.

Which **two** different categories of key influences have impacted on Thomas' involvement in physical activity? **(2)**

1 Resources ✓

2 Image ✓

> Ensure you read the question carefully; it is looking for a 'category of key influences'.

(Total for Question 4 = 2 marks)

5 Identify **three different** components of skill-related fitness that would be relevant to all the performers in **Figure 2**.

Figure 2

Component 1 Speed ✓ **(1)**

Component 2 Balance ✓ **(1)**

Component 3 Coordination ✓ **(1)**

> You could also have written 'power' as one of the components.
> Do not use the same component twice.

(Total for Question 5 = 3 marks)

6 (a) Describe the tests shown in **Figure 3** and give an example from a physical activity that would benefit from the results of each test.

5 metres

10 metres

start   finish

Test 1   Test 2

Figure 3

1 The Illinois Agility Run is used to test agility. ✓ Performers have to run around the coned course in the shortest time possible. A football coach may find the results of the test useful as agility is a component of fitness used a lot in football, ✓ for example moving quickly to dodge a player with the ball. ✓ **(3)**

2 The Standing Stork test is used to test balance. ✓ Performers have to stand in the position shown for as long as they can. A gymnastics coach is likely to benefit from the results of this test. ✓ Gymnasts use balance often, particularly on the beam where they need to perform complex routines without falling off. ✓ **(3)**

(b) Explain why a sprinter is unlikely to use the 12-minute Cooper run. **(3)**

A sprinter is unlikely to use this test as it is a test of cardiovascular endurance, ✓ which is a component of fitness not used during sprinting. Sprinting is an anaerobic exercise, whereas running for extended periods of time, e.g. 12 minutes, is aerobic. ✓ This means that the test would not be specific to the sport and therefore useless. A sprinter is more likely to use the 30-metre sprint or ruler drop test to test components related to sprinting. ✓

(Total for Question 6 = 9 marks)

7 The performers in **Figure 4** have the same body type (somatotype).

Figure 4

(a) Name the body type of the performers in **Figure 4**. **(1)**

Endomorph ✓

(b) Describe a characteristic of this body type. **(1)**

> Other answers are: Fatness
> Pear shaped body

Wide hips and narrow shoulders ✓

(c) Give **two** different advantages of this body type, one for each performer below:

(i) The sumo wrestler **(1)**

Endomorphs can use their weight to overpower opponents. ✓

(ii) The rugby prop **(1)**

Props can use their added weight to resist their opponents. ✓

Optimum weight varies for different athletic activities.

(d) Explain the term 'optimum weight' and give an example of how optimum weight can affect performance. **(3)**

Optimum weight is the most favourable weight for that activity. ✓ Each sports person has a weight at which they perform best and they try and stay at that weight. ✓ For example, a rugby prop's optimum weight would be far heavier than that of a gymnast on the pommel horse. ✓

(Total for Question 7 = 7 marks)

8 (a) Diuretics are a category of performance-enhancing drugs. Name a sport where a performer might be tempted to take this drug and explain how it might be used to improve performance. **(2)**

Boxers ✓ might be tempted to take diuretics to lose weight. They may do this to get into a lighter category. ✓

> You could also have written:
> Diuretics – Reduce concentration of other drugs. Remove fluid from the body.
> Can hide other drug use.
> Help to reduce weight.

(b) State **two** negative effects of taking diuretics. **(2)**

People who take diuretics may get dehydrated. ✓ Kidney failure. ✓

> You could also have written nausea, headaches or heart failure.

(Total for Question 8 = 4 marks)

9 Participating in activities like hockey, shown in **Figure 5**, involves risk.

Figure 5

Other than pulling a muscle, identify a **risk** that could be associated with this activity and a **measure** that could be used to reduce this risk.

Risk: **(1)**

You could get hit by another player's stick. ✓

Measure to reduce risk: **(1)**

Hockey players wear shin pads in order to provide cushioning impact when the leg gets hit. ✓

(Total for Question 9 = 2 marks)

5

6

7

8

10   Mohammed plays football for the school team.

Mohammed is three weeks into his six-week personal exercise programme (PEP). In one circuit training session he measured his heart rate (HR): before he started the session, half an hour into his session and 15 minutes after his training session.

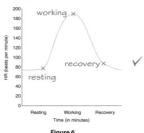

Figure 6

(a)   Plot on the graph where you think each of the following heart rate values should go: 77, 87, 189.   **(1)**

(b)   Explain why you chose the HR values in that order.   [You could mention oxygen debt.]   **(3)**

...Resting HR would be lowest value, as no physical activity is taking place...
...so there is less demand on the heart to pump blood containing oxygen. ✓
...Working HR would be the highest value because the heart has to work...
...harder to pump more oxygenated blood to the working muscles. ✓
...Recover HR is a higher value than resting HR because after 15 minutes...
...the heart is still working at a faster rate to provide oxygenated blood...
...to muscles to remove lactic acid and to pay back oxygen debt. ✓

(c)   Explain why a professional marathon runner may have a lower resting heart rate than Mohammed.   **(2)**

...The heart is a muscle, so with more training it becomes stronger. A...
...stronger heart is more efficient as it is able to pump more blood in one...
...beat. ✓ A marathon runner would have a bigger, stronger heart as a...
...result of adapting to endurance training. ✓

(Total for Question 10 = 6 marks)

9

11   (a)   Identify **two** long-term effects of regular participation in physical activity on the respiratory system.   **(2)**

1 Increased number of alveoli ✓
2 Increased lung volume ✓

(b)   Give an example of a performer who would benefit from **one** long-term effect identified in (a).   **(1)**

...Long-distance runner ✓

(c)   Explain why they would benefit from this.   **(3)**

A long-distance runner would benefit from increased lung volume...
because it means that they can take in more oxygen. Also, more...
oxygen is extracted and can get to the working muscles. ✓ With more...
oxygen the long-distance runner can improve their cardiovascular...
endurance and their performance. ✓
It also means that more waste products are released. ✓

(Total for Question 11 = 6 marks)

10

12   **Figure 7** shows the knee joint. In the table:

(a)   State the **type** of joint at the knee.   **(1)**

(b)   State **one** range of movement at this joint.   **(1)**

(c)   Give **two** specific sporting examples where this range of movement is used at this joint.   **(2)**

	Type of joint	Range of movement at this joint	Specific sporting example where this range of movement is used at this joint
Figure 7	Knee – hinge joint. ✓	Knee – extension and flexion. ✓ [Reminder: Ensure you write extension and flexion.]	Knee – kicking a ball in football. ✓ Sprinting – bringing the knee up during each stride. ✓

(Total for Question 12 = 4 marks)

11

13   Nicola is a personal trainer. She is working with a group of boxers aiming to improve their health and fitness.

(a)   Define the terms 'health' and 'fitness'.   **(2)**

...Fitness means to be able to meet the demands of the environment. ✓
Health is physical, social and mental well-being and being free...
from disease. ✓

At the start of the six-week programme Nicola issued the boxers with a PAR-Q test.

(b)   What is the purpose of a PAR-Q?   **(1)**

It is important to know whether a person is healthy enough to take...
part in different activities without getting injured. ✓

(c)   Nicola must consider SMART goals when planning the boxers' programme.

Explain how ensuring goals are realistic and time-bound can help Nicola plan an effective programme for the boxers.   **(4)**

Nicola must ensure each of the boxers' goals are realistic. ✓ A realistic goal...
is one that is possible, given all the factors involved. For example, increasing...
the amount of punches they can do in one minute from 60 to 65. ✓
In order to see if the boxers' training is having the correct effect, it is...
important to have time-bound goals. This means that each goal is given...
a time frame for completion. ✓ For example, to increase the number of...
punches in one minute from 60 to 65 by 6th September this year. ✓

(d)   Nicola believes that circuit training should be part of the boxers' training programme.

Describe how circuit training can be used to improve health and fitness.   **(3)**

Can include both aerobic and anaerobic activities. ✓
Uses a wide range of exercises. ✓
It can combine a number of components of fitness in one session. ✓

[You could also have written:
Equipment need not be expensive.
Uses the principle of progressive overload.]

(Total for Question 13 = 10 marks)

12

14 Fred is a GCSE PE student. He is a keen hockey player.

Fred is starting to plan his personal exercise programme (PEP).

Discuss the use of the principles of training when planning a PEP. **(6)**

A person must take into account their individual needs when planning a programme. This means they must consider their targets, sport and body build to ensure that the programme they complete is not too hard or inappropriate. ✓

Specificity is important as different sports require different training requirements. Fred will need a very different training regime than a boxer or gymnast as hockey requires different components of fitness. For hockey Fred needs to consider agility and speed. He must ensure that his training programme considers the needs of hockey. ✓ ✓

Progressive overload is very important. This will enable Fred to improve. Progressive overload means to gradually increase the amount of training to more than a person normally does. ✓ It can be achieved by increasing the frequency, intensity, time and type (FITT) of the activity. For example, Fred may choose to decrease the rest time in between intervals when interval training. ✓

Rest and recovery are very important when planning a programme. Fred must ensure he rests in between sessions to enable muscular adaptation to occur. A good time to do this is after a hard game or training session. ✓

> Ensure you describe the repair of the muscles and not just a general repair of the body.

> Note that full credit can only be given where answers are developed with appropriate reasons and examples.

13

15 Diet can have an impact on the body systems.

Explain the impact of diet on the cardiovascular and skeletal systems. **(6)**

Diet can have a huge impact on the cardiovascular and skeletal systems. A poor diet can cause an increase in cholesterol. This can cause an increase in blood pressure. The narrowing of the arteries can increase the risk of coronary heart disease. An increase in blood pressure to a dangerous level can put increased strain on your arteries and heart. ✓ ✓

Diet can impact the skeletal system. Eating a balanced calcium-rich diet makes bones grow and increase in density making them strong. Calcium can be found in milk and cheese. Vitamin D helps the body absorb calcium and is found in eggs and oily fish. Increased bone density allows the bones to be stronger. This prevents bones from fracturing easily. A poor diet with little calcium or vitamin D can make bones brittle. This means in a game of football, brittle bones would get injured more easily during a tackle. ✓ ✓

A healthy balanced diet consisting of the correct amounts of macro- and micronutrients provides the cardiovascular and skeletal systems with adequate nutrients and energy to enable them to function properly. Macronutrients are carbohydrates, protein and fat. All macronutrients are needed; however, too much fat can cause high cholesterol. Micronutrients are vitamins, minerals, water and fibre. Calcium is a mineral. ✓ ✓

(Total for Question 15 = 6 marks)

TOTAL FOR PAPER = 80 MARKS

> Note that full credit can only be given where answers are developed with appropriate reasons and examples.

14

1 **(a)** Which **one** of the following statements correctly defines the term 'health'? (1)

- ☐ **A** The ability to meet the demands of the environment
- ☐ **B** Completing exercise on a regular basis
- ☒ **C** State of complete mental, physical and social well-being, not merely the ✓ absence of disease and infirmity
- ☐ **D** Feeling physically fit and well

(b) **Figure 1** shows the sports participation pyramid.

Which letter, **A**, **B**, **C** or **D**, represents the stage where participants regularly experience coaching in their specific sport? (1)

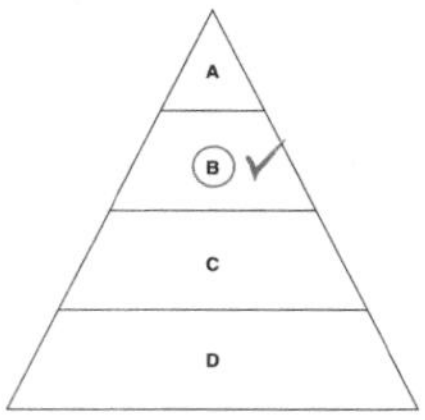

Figure 1

(c) Which **one** of the following performers would consider the endomorph somatotype to be the **most** appropriate body type for their activity? (1)

- ☐ **A** 800m runner
- ☒ **B** Shot putter ✓
- ☐ **C** Long jumper
- ☐ **D** 100m runner

(d) Which **one** of the following is a short-term effect of participation in exercise on the respiratory system? (1)

- ☐ **A** Increased build-up of lactic acid
- ☒ **B** Increased breathing rate ✓
- ☐ **C** Increased heart rate
- ☐ **D** Decreased vital capacity

> Ensure you read the question carefully. Respiratory system is the key term.

(e) Which **one** of the following is **not** an aspect of skill-related fitness? (1)

- ☐ **A** Agility
- ☐ **B** Balance
- ☒ **C** Flexibility ✓
- ☐ **D** Power

(f) Which **one** of the following training methods would be **most** beneficial to a long-distance runner? (1)

- ☐ **A** Circuit
- ☒ **B** Continuous ✓
- ☐ **C** Cross
- ☐ **D** Weight

(g) Despite the risks, some performers take drugs to improve their performance.

Which **one** of the following statements correctly links the performance-enhancing drug with its effect and a performer who would benefit from this effect? (1)

- ☐ **A** Peptide hormones taken by a snooker player to reduce anxiety levels
- ☒ **B** Stimulants taken by a boxer to increase aggression ✓
- ☐ **C** Anabolic steroids taken by a boxer to speed up weight loss
- ☐ **D** Narcotic analgesics taken by a cyclist to increase oxygen delivery during a long-distance event

(h) Which **one** of the following muscles is contracting to allow the bowler in **Figure 2** to extend his arm at the elbow? (1)

- ☐ **A** Deltoid
- ☐ **B** Biceps
- ☒ **C** Triceps ✓
- ☐ **D** Pectorals

> Look carefully at the picture. It can give you clues.

Figure 2

(i) Muscular hypertrophy is one training adaptation that occurs as a result of long-term training.

Which **one** of the following methods of training is **most** likely to cause muscular hypertrophy? (1)

- ☐ **A** Continuous
- ☐ **B** Circuit
- ☒ **C** Weight ✓
- ☐ **D** Cross

(j) Sports performers injure themselves occasionally.

Which **one** of the following is **not** an example of a type of fracture? (1)

- ☐ **A** Greenstick
- ☐ **B** Compound
- ☐ **C** Stress
- ☒ **D** Compress ✓

(Total for Question 1 = 10 marks)

2 A sports centre is doing its annual data collection, aiming to find out which facilities are used most. The table below represents the data.

(a) Complete the table, explaining how each activity could provide the stated classification of benefit. (4)

> Ensure you only give one response for each activity to avoid wasting time.

Activity	How many people use it in a month	Main age range	Classification of benefit	Explanation of how stated benefit achieved
Swimming	436	25–30	Physical	They will increase their cardiovascular fitness if the swimming session is at least 20 minutes in duration and if they go regularly. ✓ ✓
Netball	189	15–20	Social	Netball is a team sport. This means they will play with others in the team, giving opportunity to go with friends or make new friends. ✓ ✓

(b) Brenda goes to the yoga class.

Describe how taking part in physical activity can make an individual feel good. (2)

Physical activity makes you feel good by increasing serotonin levels. ✓ Regular activity also improves fitness. Losing weight through taking part in physical activity can make you feel good. ✓

> You could also mention an increase in self-esteem.

(c) The sports centre is currently running a 'two for one' deal on classes. Brenda has decided to try out the aerobics class.

Identify which key influence may have led Brenda to take part. (1)

Socioeconomic factors ✓

(Total for Question 2 = 7 marks)

3 The required components of skill-related fitness vary for different activities.

In the table:

(a) Identify the **two** most important skill-related components for each performer. (4)

(b) State how your first chosen component for each performer is used in her activity. (2)

	Component choice one	Component choice two	How first-choice component for each performer is used in her activity
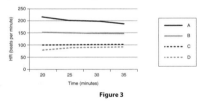 Gymnast	Balance ✓ [Ensure you do not state the same component twice.]	Power ✓	A gymnast would need balance on the beam so they do not fall off. ✓
Sprinter	Reaction time ✓ [Give a specific example of how the performer would use the component in that event.]	Speed ✓	Reaction time is needed at the start when the gun goes off. ✓

(Total for Question 3 = 6 marks)

4 Tom is a GCSE PE student. He is using interval training to improve his performance in sprinting.

(a) State **two** characteristics of interval training. (2)

Training that involves periods of work and periods of rest. ✓
Work is at a high intensity due to rest periods. ✓

(b) Tom applies the principle of progressive overload to his training.

(i) Describe the principle of 'progressive overload'. (1)

Progressive overload means to gradually increase the amount of
work in training so that fitness gains can occur. ✓

[Ensure your answers are specific. Students often give vague answers to questions on principles of training..]

(ii) State why the principle of progressive overload should be applied. (1)

It allows improvements to be made without injury occurring. ✓

(c) If Tom stopped training, he might experience reversibility.

Explain the term 'reversibility' and how it could impact Tom's performance in sprinting. (3)

Reversibility means that when you stop training any change or
improvement that has occurred due to training will decline. ✓ For
Tom it will mean that his time may increase ✓ in his race if he has a
break from training. ✓

[In the past students have confused reversibility with rest and recovery. Read the question carefully.]

(Total for Question 4 = 7 marks)

5 Amreet is a 30-year-old interested in improving her health and fitness.

Figure 3

(a) Which of the lines on the graph in **Figure 3** (**A**, **B**, **C** or **D**) would Amreet use to make sure she was working within her target zone? (1)

B. ✓

(b) Explain your choice. [MHR = 220 minus age.] (3)

Amreet must work within 60-80% of her maximum HR to be within
her target zone. ✓ At 30 Amreet must ensure her heart is beating
between 114 and 152 beats per minute. B shows she is working
between 114 and 152, demonstrating she is working within her
target zone for her age. ✓ Line A is too high and lines C and D are
too low. ✓

(Total for Question 5 = 4 marks)

6 (a) Explain the term 'anorexia'. (2)

Anorexia is an eating disorder. It causes extreme weight loss by refusal
to eat or eating very little. ✓ The lack of nutrients can cause fatigue and
dehydration. ✓

(b) Explain **one** impact of being obese on achieving sustained involvement in physical activity. (3)

Being obese places additional pressure on body systems due to
excess weight. ✓ The excess weight will place additional pressure
on joints, causing injury or lack of flexibility. ✓ This means that the
performer will have difficulty sustaining activities such as walking or
running. ✓

[Make sure you state how being obese affects involvement in physical activity, not just how it affects everyday life.]

(Total for Question 6 = 5 marks)

7 Diet and rest need to be considered when planning a healthy active lifestyle.

Describe the impact of diet and rest on the muscular system.

[Ensure you read the question. It is asking for benefits to the *muscular* system.]

(a) Impact of **diet** on the muscular system (2)

Protein in your diet helps the growth and repair of muscles. ✓
Lack of protein can cause muscle damage. ✓

(b) Impact of **rest** on the muscular system [Rest can allow for muscle growth.] (2)

Adequate rest is essential to the muscular system; it allows the
muscles to recover. ✓ Only while resting can adaptations occur in
the muscles. Without adequate rest, muscles can become damaged.
However, too much rest can cause muscular atrophy to occur. ✓

(Total for Question 7 = 4 marks)

8   Although not illegal, alcohol and smoking do have dangerous side effects on the body.

Identify **two** possible health risks for each recreational drug in the table.   (4)

Recreational drug	Negative effect one	Negative effect two
Alcohol Other answers include: Increased blood pressure and increased weight.	Heart failure ✓	Liver disease ✓
Smoking Other answers include: Bronchitis, blood clot and emphysema.	Stroke ✓	Lung cancer ✓

(Total for Question 8 = 4 marks)

9   Charlotte and Amit both compete in rugby.

Using an example, explain how balanced competition can reduce risk in physical activity.   (3)

By balancing the competition by age ✓ in rugby, it prevents older or more developed athletes playing younger and smaller athletes. ✓ Athletes are less likely to receive a fracture as a result of impact in a tackle. ✓

Other good examples include:
Boxing – weight categories.
Judo – different belts competing against each other.

(Total for Question 9 = 3 marks)

10   Increased stroke volume is a long-term effect of regular participation in physical activity on the cardiovascular system.

Describe **two** other long-term effects of regular participation in physical activity on the cardiovascular system.

Long-term effect 1   (2)

Increased capillarisation means that there is an increased blood flow ✓ supplying oxygen to the working muscles. ✓

Long-term effect 2   (2)

Lower resting heart rate means a more efficient heart. ✓ The heart beats less often to eject the same amount of blood. ✓

(Total for Question 10 = 4 marks)

11   Oxygen debt is a short-term effect of participation in exercise.

(a)   Explain the term 'oxygen debt'.   (3)

Oxygen debt is the extra ✓ amount of oxygen consumed after a period of anaerobic activity ✓ compared with the amount which would have originally been consumed in the same time at rest. This results in shortfall of oxygen. ✓

Ensure you apply the key feature of oxygen debt being linked with anaerobic work. Also make sure you use the correct terms, e.g. oxygen NOT air.

(b)   For an activity of your choice, identify when the performer would experience oxygen debt in their activity.   (1)

Ensure your example is specific to the sport.

Name of activity ..... Boxing

A series of powerful, explosive punches. ✓

(Total for Question 11 = 4 marks)

12   **Figure 4** shows an athlete clearing a hurdle.

Figure 4

Complete the statements below by identifying which muscles are contracting to allow the hurdler to achieve the described actions.

(a)   Straightening the leg over the hurdle   (1)

Quadriceps ✓

(b)   Bending the trailing leg going over the hurdle   (1)

Hamstrings ✓

(Total for Question 12 = 2 marks)

13   The skeletal system has several functions.

(a)   Using an example from sport, describe how the skeleton gives protection.   (3)

The skeleton provides protection of your vital organs, ✓ for example your heart and brain. ✓ For example, in boxing your skull prevents your brain being damaged when you are punched. ✓

The skeleton also aids movement.

Other examples include:
Football – Ribs protecting your heart when hit by the ball.

(b)   Identify the range of movement at the following joints.

(i)   Shoulder   (1)

Adduction, abduction, rotation, flexion and extension. ✓

(ii)   Knee   (1)

Ensure you include both as the question is asking for the 'range' at the knee.

Flexion and extension ✓

(c)   (i)   Identify **one** effect of regular participation in physical activity on the skeletal system.   (1)

Increased strength of ligaments ✓

(ii)   For a named sport, state **one** way in which the effect you have identified in (c) (i) can benefit the performer.   (1)

An example of this would be in football, where you are less likely to incur an injury if tackled when your joints are more stable due to stronger ligaments. ✓

(d)   Bones become lighter and lose density with age. Give an example of how performers can delay the onset of osteoporosis.   (1)

Weight-bearing activities such as walking can delay the onset of osteoporosis ✓

Activities such as weight lifting, cycling and rowing would not be credited.

(Total for Question 13 = 8 marks)

14   Using examples of relevant agencies, discuss the common purposes of initiatives developed to provide opportunities for becoming or remaining involved in physical activity.   (6)

Initiatives are set up in order to encourage people to take part in physical activity. The aims of these initiatives are to increase participation, retain people and to create opportunities. Two common roles of agencies include increasing and sustaining participation at the foundation stage of sports participation and providing opportunities for talented sports people to excel. ✓ Also, they provide activities and funding to allow children to get involved in activities such as swimming and multi-sports days; ✓ and give discounts to older adults, allowing them to take part at a reduced rate. There are three agencies that aim to provide opportunities for this to happen. They include Sport England, the Youth Sport Trust and national governing bodies of different sports. Sport England aims to deliver a mass participation sporting legacy from the 2012 Olympic and Paralympic Games through the Places People Play initiative. ✓ An example of how the Youth Sport Trust provides opportunities for young people to engage in PE is the links they establish between schools and national governing bodies to create new clubs on school sites. ✓ For example, initiating links between the school netball team and the local league teams. National governing bodies increase the skills level of those participating in sport by organising more opportunities for people of all levels to compete and providing financial help with facility development. ✓ For example, Badminton England may fund a local Badminton centre. In conclusion, there are many initiatives set up by all agencies to encourage and support people taking part in exercise. ✓

Note that full credit can only be given where answers are developed with appropriate reasons and examples.

(Total for Question 14 = 6 marks)

27

15   Some sports performers choose to take performance-enhancing drugs although these are illegal.

Discuss the use of erythropoietin / EPO for enhancing performance.   (6)

EPO is a performance-enhancing drug that can help increase red blood cell production. ✓ This means that there is an increase in the amount of oxygen being delivered to working muscles. EPO would aid long-distance athletes, for example marathon runners or long-distance cyclists, because these activities require an increase in oxygen delivery to maintain performance levels over the duration of the event. ✓ The increase in red blood cells enables these athletes to maintain a good energy supply throughout the race ✓ as more energy is released using oxygen, allowing them to maintain a good pace and cover the distance more quickly than they would have done. ✓ However, EPO does have side effects. ✓ These include increased risk of heart attacks, deep-vein thrombosis and strokes, all due to the increase in the thickness of blood. All of these negative side effects greatly increase the risk of the user dying younger. In conclusion, an athlete using EPO would have an unfair advantage over other athletes in the race. ✓

Note that full credit can only be given where answers are developed with appropriate reasons and examples.

(Total for Question 15 = 6 marks)

TOTAL FOR PAPER = 80 MARKS

28

Full Course Paper 3   Answers

1 (a) Which **one** of the following is an example of a 'resources' key influence that can impact on achieving sustained involvement in physical activity? **(1)**

- A Role models
- B Fashion
- ☒ C Location ✓
- D Disability

(b) Initiatives such as Sport England aim to contribute to the development of healthy lifestyles. Which of the following is **not** an aim of initiatives? **(1)**

- A Retain people in physical activity
- B Create opportunities for participation
- C Increase participation in physical activity
- ☒ D Increase earning potential of elite athletes ✓

(c) Which of the following is the correct definition of muscular endurance? **(1)**

- A The amount of force a muscle can exert against a resistance
- ☒ B The ability to use voluntary muscles many times without getting tired ✓
- C The ability to exercise the entire body for long periods of time without tiring
- D The ability to do strength performances quickly

(d) Which of the following is **not** a test of cardiovascular fitness? **(1)**

- A Treadmill test
- B Harvard step test
- ☒ C 30-metre sprint ✓
- D Cooper's 12-minute run test

(e) Which of the performers in the following statements is applying the principle of specificity? **(1)**

- ☒ A A tennis player practising their first serves ✓
- B A track sprinter doing interval training in the swimming pool
- C A shot putter taking part in continuous training
- D A basketball player working on their speed at the track

(f) Which of the following statements correctly describes blood flow during exercise? **(1)**

- A Blood flow to the digestive system is lower at rest than when exercising.
- B Blood flow is distributed equally between the muscular system and the digestive system at rest and when exercising.
- ☒ C Blood flow to the digestive system is greater at rest than when exercising. ✓
- D Blood flow to the muscular system is lower during exercise than at rest.

(g) Which of the following is **not** a factor that can affect optimum weight? **(1)**

- A Height
- B Gender
- C Muscle girth
- ☒ D Consumption of fat in diet ✓

(h) **Figure 1** shows a long-distance runner's heart rate during a 10-kilometre race.

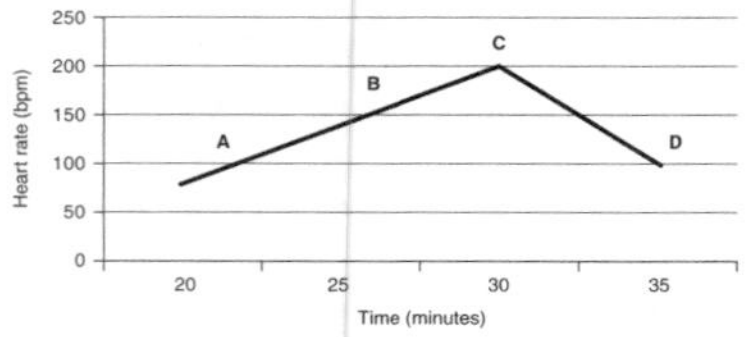

Figure 1

Using **Figure 1**, at which point, **A, B, C** or **D**, does the performer begin to apply the principle of rest and recovery? **(1)**

- A
- B
- C
- ☒ D ✓

(i) Which of the following is a short-term effect of exercise on the muscular system? **(1)**

- A Increased breathing rate
- ☒ B Increased production of lactic acid ✓
- C Muscular hypertrophy
- D Increased strength of ligaments and tendons

(j) **Figure 2** shows a performer on the trampoline performing the pike jump.

Figure 2

Which of the following muscles flexes the trunk to create the pike position? **(1)**

- A Latissimus dorsi
- B Trapezius
- C Deltoid
- ☒ D Abdominals ✓

(Total for Question 1 = 10 marks)

2 **Figure 3** shows the sports participation pyramid.

'Elite' is also known as excellence.

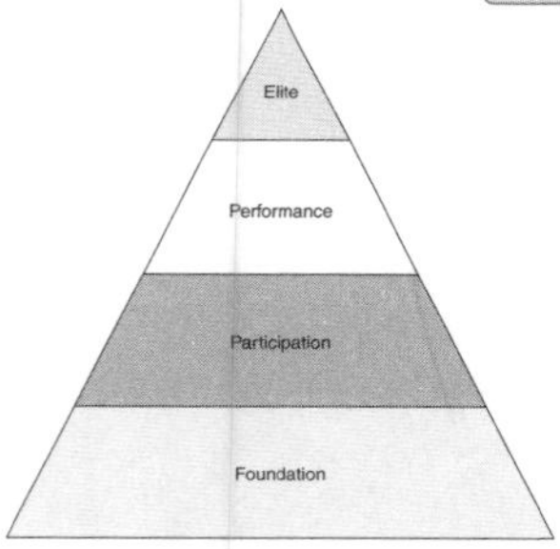

Figure 3

(a) Explain why the elite stage of the sports participation pyramid has the **smallest** number of participants. **(3)**

The elite level of the sports participation pyramid is only for a limited number of people with the correct skills and determination to reach this level. ✓ Not all performers who have the correct level of skill will reach this level as they may not have the determination or train as hard. ✓ Not all people have the ability to become elite. Also, some performers may not have access to coaching at that level. ✓

(b) Describe how physical activity allows people to remain involved in sport when they are no longer able to be a performer. **(2)**

If a person is injured and cannot take part as a performer they can use their knowledge as a coach ✓ or volunteer. ✓

(Total for Question 2 = 5 marks)

82

3 Complete the table below by giving an example of how flexibility would be used by each performer. (3)

Performer	How flexibility is used in their activity
Hurdler	A hurdler would use flexibility to achieve the correct position and height over the hurdle by lifting his leg. ✓
Gymnast	A gymnast would use flexibility to perform specific movements more easily within a routine, such as the splits without getting injured. ✓
Tennis player	A tennis player would use flexibility to return shots from the edges of the court. ✓

(Total for Question 3 = 3 marks)

4 Mrs Sharma is a PE teacher. She is concerned about the health of some of the sixth form students. She has decided to set up a lunchtime badminton club. Mrs Sharma gives all pupils a physical activity readiness questionnaire (PAR-Q) at the start of the term.

(a) Give an example of a 'typical' question that might be asked on a PAR-Q. (1)

Do you have high blood pressure? ✓

> Other examples include:
> Do you smoke?
> What is your weight?
> Do you have any known health problems?
> Does anyone in your family have high blood pressure?

(b) Mrs Sharma believes that the sixth form students' health will be improved by taking part in exercise.

Explain the term 'health'. (2)

Health is a state of complete mental, physical and social well-being and not merely the absence of disease and infirmity. ✓ If one is missing, you are not completely healthy. For example, a performer may be physically fit but extremely stressed so not fulfilling the mental aspect and not completely healthy. ✓

(c) Before each badminton game Mrs Sharma leads a warm-up.

Explain the purpose of a 'warm-up'. (3)

Warm-ups physically and mentally prepare you for exercise. ✓ They also increase oxygen delivery to the working muscles. ✓ A warm-up helps you rehearse in your head the skills that you are about to use. It can increase the temperature of your muscles, tendons and ligaments, reducing the chance of injury. ✓

(Total for Question 4 = 6 marks)

5 When setting goals to plan involvement in physical activity, it is important to apply the principles of SMART targets.

(a) Explain why it is important that each target is 'specific'. (2)

It is important that goals are specific to provide the performer with a focus to improve upon. ✓ Focus helps performers to stay on track. Just 'to improve' is too vague; performers must state how they are going to improve. ✓

(b) Give **one** example of a 'measurable' goal. (1)

To be able to run 1 second faster in the 30m sprint. ✓

> Saying 'To run the 30m sprint faster' is too vague.

(Total for Question 5 = 3 marks)

6 (a) Explain the importance of macronutrients in maintaining a healthy active lifestyle. (3)

Macronutrients are carbohydrates, fats and protein. ✓ Carbohydrates and fats provide energy. ✓ Fats also provide insulation. This energy is used to allow us to be active. Protein is used for muscle growth and repair. ✓

> Do not use abbreviations such as 'carbs'.

(b) Explain why it is important to consider the timing of dietary intake when performing exercise. (2)

If we do not leave enough time between eating and exercising, our digestive system does not have enough time to digest the food and this can cause discomfort. ✓ If the food is not completely digested, we may not have the energy required to exercise at the correct level. ✓

(Total for Question 6 = 5 marks)

7 Despite the risks, some performers take drugs to enhance their performance.

In the table:

(a) Identify **one** possible health risk of taking each performance-enhancing drug. (3)

Performance-enhancing drug	Health risk
Diuretics	Severe dehydration ✓
Anabolic steroids	Liver damage ✓
Narcotic analgesics	Depression ✓

(b) Using an example, explain why a performer might risk using beta blockers to enhance performance. (3)

Performers might risk taking beta blockers to increase their chances of winning by reducing anxiety and helping them stay calm. ✓ For example, a snooker player ✓ might take them to steady their hand when taking a shot to ensure the ball goes into the pocket. ✓

(Total for Question 7 = 6 marks)

8   **Figure 4** shows Will during a continuous training session in preparation for his next marathon.

Figure 4

(a)   Explain why Will would choose this method of training.   (2)

Continuous training develops cardiovascular and muscular endurance. ✓ Both of these health-related components are required in marathon running. ✓

(b)   State whether continuous training is aerobic or anaerobic.   (1)

Aerobic ✓

(c)   Describe how Will could apply **two** of the components of the FITT training principle to his continuous training.   (4)

Will could apply the principle of time to his continuous training by increasing the amount of time he spends running. ✓ This would allow him to progressively improve his cardiovascular fitness. For example, increasing his run from 35 to 40 minutes. ✓ He could also apply the principle of frequency by increasing the amount of times he trains in a week from twice to three times. ✓ By increasing the amount of times he runs his body will adapt to cope with more intensity during a race. ✓

(Total for Question 8 = 7 marks)

9   Shania plays hockey for the school team. It is important she wears shin pads to prevent injury.

State **two** other ways that Shania could avoid injury.   (2)

1 Ensuring she completes an adequate warm-up ✓

2 Adhering to the rules of hockey ✓

(Total for Question 9 = 2 marks)

37

10   Jai is a keen volleyball player. During a match his blood pressure and heart rate increase.

(a)   Explain why the cardiovascular system responds in this way when beginning exercise.   (4)

Heart rate increases because

Ensure you link to the cardiovascular system.

By increasing HR there is increased oxygen ✓ delivery to the working muscles and increased removal of carbon dioxide. ✓

Blood pressure increases because

Blood pressure increases due to increased speed of blood flow ✓ and greater strength of contraction of the heart as the heart speeds up to provide more oxygenated blood to the muscles. ✓

(b)   Jai ensures he has a day off training after a match.

Explain the impact of rest on Jai's cardiovascular system.   (2)

Rest allows the heart to return to its resting heart rate. ✓ The heart is a muscle. Resting allows muscular hypertrophy of the heart, allowing it to become stronger. ✓

(Total for Question 10 = 6 marks)

11   Describe the impact of smoking on a long-distance runner's performance.   (2)

Smoking causes a reduction in oxygen uptake by the red blood cells. They will carry carbon monoxide from the cigarette smoke in preference to oxygen. ✓ This means that less oxygen will get to the working muscles during a race. This means that during a race less oxygen will be able to get to the working muscles and therefore the runner will not be as effective. ✓

(Total for Question 11 = 2 marks)

Remember it is reduced *uptake* of oxygen, not *intake*.

38

12   Sameleh takes part in the school sports day in three events. He has been observing elite athletes in each of his events.

Identify which muscles are contracting to achieve the actions in **Figure 5**.   (3)

Keeping the arm straight at the elbow in the shot put

Tricep ✓

Keeping the leg straight at the knee in the pole vault

Quadriceps ✓

Moving the arm away from the mid-line of the body in the discus

Deltoid ✓

Figure 5

(Total for Question 12 = 3 marks)

39

13   The skeletal system plays an important role in allowing for a healthy active lifestyle. **Figure 6** shows the skeletal system of a football player preparing to kick the ball.

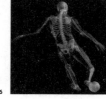

Figure 6

(a)   Identify **three** functions of the skeletal system in use during physical activity.   (3)

1 Protection ✓

2 Movement ✓

3 Support ✓

(b)   Give **one** example of how each function is used during a football game.   (3)

1 The skull protects the player's brain during a header. ✓

2 The skeleton forms joints to enable players to move to kick the ball. ✓

3 The skeleton provides a frame for the body. This allows a goalkeeper to stand strong in the goal. ✓

Ensure you give linked examples to the function.

(Total for Question 13 = 6 marks)

14   Describe **two** named types of fracture.   (4)

1 Compound fractures are where a broken bone ✓ causes the skin to break. ✓

2 Greenstick fractures are when the bone bends on one side ✓ and breaks on the other. ✓

You could have also mentioned stress and simple fractures.

(Total for Question 14 = 4 marks)

40

15 Using examples, explain how taking part in physical activity can stimulate cooperation and physical challenge. (6)

An activity that pushes you to your boundaries can stimulate physical challenge. ✓ An example is a marathon. ✓ It is a huge physical challenge to run 26.2 miles because of all the training you will have had to complete prior to the event to increase your fitness to a suitable level. Also, you need the mental strength to keep going in training and make the necessary adjustments to your normal life to make time for training. ✓

Playing for a team can stimulate cooperation. ✓ Teams that work well together are able to use good communication skills and demonstrate good teamwork. It enables people to find solutions and work together on tasks. ✓ A netball team that cooperates well with each other and communicates when things go wrong and congratulates people when things go right provides a good grounding for a successful team. ✓

Note that full credit can only be given where answers are developed with appropriate reasons and examples.

(Total for Question 15 = 6 marks)

41

16 Paul is a long-distance runner and Alana is a sprinter. They are both sixteen years old.

Explain how they would use heart rate target zones within their training. (6)

Target heart rate zones are used to maximise fitness adaptations. The heart rate at which Paul and Alana will improve for their event is different. ✓ This is because Paul will concentrate on improving his cardiovascular fitness and Alana will concentrate on improving her speed. ✓
In order to improve his cardiovascular fitness Paul will need to work within the aerobic training zone. His aerobic training zone is between 60 and 80% of his maximum heart rate. ✓
220 – 16 = 204
80 x 204/100 = 163
60 x 204/100 = 122
Paul will need to work between 122 and 163 in order to improve his cardiovascular fitness.
In order to improve her speed, Alana will need to focus her training on working within the anaerobic training zone. Her anaerobic training zone is between 80 and 90% of her maximum heart rate. ✓
163
90 x 204/100 = 183
Alana will need to work between 163 and 183 to improve her speed. ✓
The percentages differ for each performer due to the different nature of the events. Aerobic training is done at a lower intensity, as is the race because it is done over a longer period of time. Aerobic exercise means 'with oxygen', so the heart needs time to supply all the oxygen the muscles need. Anaerobic exercise takes place without oxygen, as with short fast bursts the heart cannot supply blood and oxygen to the muscles as fast as the cells use them. ✓

Note that full credit can only be given where answers are developed with appropriate reasons and examples.

(Total for Question 16 = 6 marks)
TOTAL FOR PAPER = 80 MARKS

42

85

1 (a) Which of the following **best** describes a healthy active lifestyle? (1)

☒ A Eating a healthy balanced diet and walking 20 minutes every day ✓

☐ B Playing in a badminton match

☐ C Playing for a local hockey team and training twice a week

☐ D Going to aerobics twice a week with friends

(b) Which **one** of the following is **not** a mental benefit of taking part in physical activity? (1)

☐ A Feeling good

☒ B Cooperation ✓

☐ C Aesthetic appreciation

☐ D Physical challenge

(c) The following statements were made by students explaining what influenced them when deciding whether or not to participate in an activity. Which of the statements relate to the category of key influence 'people'? (1)

☐ A Whether the activity is within walking distance of your house

☐ B Whether you have a long-term illness

☐ C Whether it has been shown on television

☒ D Whether your friends like the activity ✓

(d) Which of the following correctly defines 'exercise'? (1)

☐ A The ability to meet the demands of the environment

☐ B To gradually increase the amount of overload so that fitness gains occur, without potential for injury

☒ C A form of physical activity done to maintain or improve health and physical fitness. It is not competitive sport. ✓

☐ D Playing sport against another team

(e) Which of the following correctly defines 'recovery'? (1)

☐ A The period of time allotted to recovery

☒ B The time required for the repair of damage to the body caused by training or competition ✓

☐ C Any adaptation that takes place as a consequence of training, which will be reversed when you stop training

☐ D The time taken over a six-week training period to ensure training goals are met

(f) Which of the following statements is a benefit of a cool-down? (1)

☒ A It aids the removal of lactic acid ✓

☐ B It slowly increases the heart rate and breathing rate

☐ C It decreases flexibility

☐ D It reduces the chance of injury during the activity

(g) Which of the following performers would consider an ectomorph somatotype to be the most appropriate body type for their activity? (1)

☐ A 100m sprinter

☐ B Hammer thrower

☒ C High jumper ✓

☐ D Shot putter

(h) If an individual had high levels of low density lipoprotein (LDL, 'bad cholesterol'), which of the following should he or she avoid in order to improve his / her health? (1)

☐ A Gentle exercise

☒ B Foods high in saturated fat ✓

☐ C Moderate exercise

☐ D Foods high in unsaturated fat (e.g. sunflower oil, nuts)

(i) Which **one** of the following is an effect of smoking on the respiratory system? (1)

☐ A Increased lung capacity

☐ B Oxygen debt

☐ C Increased breathing rate

☒ D Reduction in oxygen uptake by red blood cells ✓

(j) Which of the following joint actions would occur as a result of the biceps contracting? (1)

☒ A Flexion ✓

☐ B Extension

☐ C Adduction

☐ D Abduction

(Total for Question 1 = 10 marks)

2 Peggy and Joan play badminton weekly as part of a healthy active lifestyle.

Figure 1 below shows Peggy and Joan deciding service before their badminton match.

Figure 1

Apart from the possible mental benefits, why else would over-50s badminton players take part in physical activity? (2)

To improve their fitness ✓

To see their friends ✓

Ensure you give answers from two different categories.

(Total for Question 2 = 2 marks)

43   44   45   46

86

3   **Figure 2** shows the sports participation pyramid.

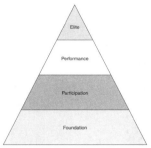

Figure 2

(a)   Explain the participation stage of the pyramid.   **(3)**

> Try not to confuse performance and participation.

...The.participation.stage.of.the.pyramid.is.when.people.choose.to.continue....
...sport.when.it.is.not.compulsory..✓.Fewer.people.are.at.this.stage.than......
...at.the.foundation.stage..Sport.is.at.a.higher.level.of.skill.but.not.as......
...competitive.as.the.performance.stage.✓.For.example,.joining.an.after-.....
...school.club.✓...

(b)   Outline how someone can move from the participation to the performance stage of the
       sports participation pyramid.   **(2)**

...By.having.specialist.coaching✓.and.entering.competitions.✓..................
....

(Total for Question 3 = 5 marks)

47

4   Health-related exercise demands can vary within sporting activities.

      Using an example, explain the importance of body composition to a performer in their activity.   **(3)**

...Body.composition.is.important.to.all.performers.as.each.activity...............
...requires.a.different.ratio.of.body.fat.to.muscle.for.their.activity.✓.........
...Boxers.require.a.high.ratio.of.muscle.to.body.fat..They.need.the................
...muscle.to.provide.the.required.strength.to.beat.their.opponent,✓..............
...if.they.had.too.much.body.fat.this.would.give.unnecessary.weight.............
...and.make.it.harder.for.them.to.move.around.the.ring.quickly..It................
...could.also.make.them.less.agile,.therefore.more.likely.to.be.struck..........
...by.their.opponent..✓...

(Total for Question 4 = 3 marks)

48

5   The Stratford family are very keen on taking part in sport. The father, Mike, is 36 and is a keen
     rugby player who plays regularly on Saturdays for the local team. Darcey, his daughter, is 16. She
     has just reached the regional under-16 tennis final.

(a)   Explain why it is important for Mike and Darcey to consider individual differences when
       developing their weight training programme.   **(2)**

...Everybody.is.different.and.therefore.requires.different.things.within...........
...their.training.in.order.to.progress..✓.An.inappropriate.training..................
...programme.for.the.individual.could.cause.injury......................................
...Men.tend.to.be.stronger.than.women,.therefore.....

> Do not get this confused with specificity!
> Individual difference is for the person.
> Specificity is for the sport.

...Darcey.should.not.be.expected.to.lift.the.same....
...weight.as.Mike.in.training.sessions..If.she.tried....
...to,.she.would.be.likely.to.injure.herself..✓...........

(b)   Describe how Mike and Darcey could use each aspect of the FITT principle to improve their
       fitness and level of performance when participating in their activities.   **(4)**

...The.FITT.principles.include.frequency,.intensity,.time.and.type..✓.Mike......
...and.Darcey.can.ensure.they.train.regularly.and.could.increase.the.amount...
...of.times.they.train.in.one.week.in.order.to.improve..✓.They.could..............
...increase.the.intensity.of.the.training.they.are.doing.to.make.sure.they.are..
...working.hard.enough.for.training.adaptations.to.take.place..An.example.of..
...this.could.be.increasing.the.weight.or.amount.of.reps.they.do......................
...They.should.make.sure.they.are.working.for.long.enough.in.each................
...session..For.example,.they.could.increase.the.amount.of.each.activity.......
...they.do,.therefore.increasing.the.time.taken.✓.......................................
...They.must.also.ensure.the.type.of.training.they.do.is.appropriate.for.......
...their.sport..In.addition.to.weight.training.to.increase.their.muscular.......
...strength,.they.both.take.part.in.fartlek.sessions.to.improve.their..............
...cardiovascular.endurance.✓...

(Total for Question 5 = 6 marks)

49

6   State **three** reasons why performers use goal setting.   **(3)**

1 Goal.setting.helps.performers.to.focus.on.what.they.need.to.improve..✓...
....

2 It.helps.to.motivate.you.to.carry.on.towards.accomplishing.your..............
   long-term.goal..✓...

3 It.helps.to.plan.your.training..✓..
....

(Total for Question 6 = 3 marks)

7   (a)   Identify **three different** training methods that could be adapted for use by a performer
            who needs high levels of power for their activity.   **(3)**

1 Circuit.training.✓...

2 Weight.training.✓..

3 Interval.training.✓...

(b)   Describe how **one** of the methods you identified in (a) could be used to improve power.   **(3)**

...Circuit.training.—.you.can.focus.each.station.on.improving.speed.and........
...strength,.for.example.burpees..✓.In.burpees.you.have.to.use.explosive......
...strength.to.jump.from.the.floor.✓.As.you.have.to.do.this.quickly.this........
...will.increase.power..You.would.be.working.anaerobically..✓....................

(Total for Question 7 = 6 marks)

50

87

Full Course Paper 4   Answers

8 (a) Explain how **two** requirements of a balanced diet can aid physical activity. **(3)**

...Carbohydrates and protein are both required in a balanced diet. Carbohydrates provide energy required to take part in physical activity. ✓ Protein is needed to repair muscles after training. ✓ Protein can help prevent injury by repairing muscles and allows us to participate again. ✓

> Look at the question command word to gauge how much detail is required.

(b) Explain why it is important to consider the timing of your dietary intake before taking part in physical activity. **(2)**

...At rest there is a greater blood flow to the digestive system so that food can be digested properly. When we exercise there is a reduction in blood flow to the digestive system in favour of the muscles that are working. ✓ This means we should not eat immediately before exercise as there will not be enough blood available to digest the food, which can cause discomfort. It is important to wait at least a couple of hours before exercising after eating. ✓

(Total for Question 8 = 5 marks)

9 (a) Define the term 'anorexia'. | Ensure you know the definitions of each weight condition. **(1)**

...A prolonged eating disorder due to loss of appetite. ✓

(b) State how any **two** symptoms of anorexia would impact on achieving sustained involvement in physical activity. **(2)**

1 If you do not eat enough you will not have enough energy to complete physical activity. ✓

2 Anorexia can cause tiredness. If you are tired you will find it hard to complete physical activity. ✓

(Total for Question 9 = 3 marks)

51

10 Complete the following table by:

Identifying a risk reduction measure relevant to the activity in **Figures 3**, **4** and **5** **(3)**

Stating how the identified risk reduction measure reduces risk associated with the activity **(3)**

Activity where used	Risk reduction measure relevant to the activity	How risk is reduced through this measure
Figure 3	Helmet ✓	Cushions the blow to the head if a rider falls off, reducing risk of concussion. ✓
Figure 4	Warm up ✓ *Be specific. Do not use the same risk for two sports.*	Increases muscle elasticity so players are less likely to pull a muscle. ✓
Figure 5	Leg pads ✓	Stops the ball hitting their legs which reduces chance of fractures by absorbing impact. ✓

(Total for Question 10 = 6 marks)

52

11 (a) The equation below is incomplete.

Complete the equation that is used to calculate the amount of blood ejected from the heart per minute. **(1)**

...Cardiac output... = ...heart rate... × stroke volume ✓

(b) A healthy active lifestyle will have an impact on the body systems. Explain **two** short-term effects of exercise on the body's cardiovascular system. **(4)**

1 When you exercise your HR increases to increase the amount of oxygen delivered to the working muscles and increase the removal of carbon dioxide. ✓✓

2 Your stroke volume also increases to increase the rate of blood flow, ensuring blood gets to the working muscles quickly. ✓✓

> Ensure you are referring to short-term and not long-term effects of exercise.

(Total for Question 11 = 5 marks)

12 Regular participation in exercise can have long-term effects on the body systems. One long-term effect of regular exercise on the respiratory system is an increased number of alveoli.

Describe the benefits of this adaptation. **(2)**

...An increased number of alveoli in the lungs means that there are more places for gaseous exchange to happen. ✓ This means that more oxygen can be extracted from the air. For athletes that rely on oxygen uptake such as long-distance runners, this will enable them to improve their performance. ✓

> Credit is given for identifying the correct performer – sprinters would not benefit from this.

(Total for Question 12 = 2 marks)

53

13 (a) Complete the table below. | Make sure you look at the word before filling in the box. **(4)**

Name of contraction	Definition of contraction	Sporting example
Isotonic contraction	Contractions that result in movement. ✓	Kicking a ball. ✓
Isometric contraction	Muscles contract but there is no movement. ✓	Stationary phase of a rugby scrum. ✓

(b) Describe the execution of a technique in an activity of your choice that is brought about by the contraction of the hamstrings. **(2)**

...Contraction of the hamstring happens when a performer in football kicks the ball. ✓ The bend in the knee forms the initial stage of the kick. ✓

(Total for Question 13 = 6 marks)

14 (a) Give an example of a ball and socket joint. | Use your body if you are unsure. **(1)**

...Shoulder ✓

(b) State the range of movement possible at a ball and socket joint. **(1)**

...Flexion, extension, rotation, adduction, abduction ✓

(c) Give a specific sporting action where this range of movement is used at this joint. **(1)**

...Backwards rotation during backstroke swimming ✓

> Give a specific example.

(Total for Question 14 = 3 marks)

54

88

15 Weight-bearing activities can increase the strength of ligaments and tendons.

Using an example, explain why stronger ligaments and tendons will be beneficial to a performer of your choice. **(3)**

During a centre pass ✓ a netball player would have more stability in their ankle joint and will therefore be able to push off with more power. ✓ It also means they are less likely to get injured through straining their ankle when changing pace or direction. ✓

(Total for Question 15 = 3 marks)

16 Discuss the use of coordination by each performer in **Figures 6**, **7** and **8**. **(6)**

| Figure 6 | Figure 7 | Figure 8 |

Golfers use coordination to ensure they time their swing correctly. ✓ Without this, their shot would either lack the required power to get the ball the necessary distance (so needing more shots to play the round), or lack the necessary accuracy so that the ball stays on the fairway and the golfer doesn't need to take extra shots to retrieve a badly aimed ball. ✓

Gymnasts use coordination to ensure they time the movements of their routines to give a rhythmic and accurate performance. ✓ Without this, they will not have the required balance on the beam and may fall off, causing a reduced mark. They also need coordination to ensure their routines show precision. Without this, the performance will not be aesthetically pleasing and will not gain the maximum amount of marks. ✓

Boxers require coordination to ensure they create the correct amount of power and accuracy in each punch so that it gains the most possible points. ✓ This prevents them from wasting energy on punches that do not reach the correct spot and therefore do not gain the maximum amount of points. They also need coordination to ensure they are agile enough to move out of the way of their opponent's punches. ✓

(Total for Question 16 = 6 marks)

17 Shuti exercises regularly to increase her fitness.

Explain the short- and long-term effects and benefits of regular exercise on the muscular system and future performance. **(6)**

Short-term effects of exercise on the muscular system include increased production of lactic acid, muscle fatigue and an increased amount of oxygen which is needed to provide the muscles with energy. ✓ As the muscles are using oxygen more quickly during exercise, they require it to be replaced quickly. Without sufficient oxygen the muscles cannot provide the required amount of energy for the exercise, and muscles tire and become less efficient. ✓ For example, during events such as the 800m in swimming, performers produce more lactic acid and the muscles get tired. This means their performance can deteriorate if there is not enough oxygen to replace what is lost. ✓ The muscles also increase in temperature, meaning they become more elastic. This means they are less likely to tear and cause injury. Regular exercise increases the strength of muscles. This aids activities that require power, strength and muscular endurance. ✓ Regular exercise also causes the muscles to increase in size. This is called muscular hypertrophy. Sprinters have increased muscle size due to strength training, which allows them to be more powerful during the race. ✓ Increased power can enable them to push off more quickly during each stride, making their race faster. Increased size and strength of the muscles can lower the risk of injury. For example, when changing direction, performers are less likely to sprain their ankle as the stronger tendons and ligaments will keep the joint in place. ✓

(Total for Question 17 = 6 marks)

TOTAL FOR PAPER = 80 MARKS

1 Which **one** of the following statements describes a physical benefit of exercise? (1)

- A Increase in serotonin
- B Increase in self-esteem
- [X] C Losing weight if overweight ✓
- D Improving cooperation skills

(Total for Question 1 = 1 mark)

2 Which of the following is **not** an example of a 'resources' key influence? (1)

- A Location
- B Access
- [X] C Cost ✓
- D Time

(Total for Question 2 = 1 mark)

3 Which of the following is an essential macronutrient in a healthy diet? (1)

- [X] A Protein ✓
- B Water
- C Fibre
- D Vitamins

(Total for Question 3 = 1 mark)

4 Olivia goes to the after-school rounders and netball club.

Which stage of the sports participation pyramid would she be considered to have reached? (1)

- A Foundation
- B Performance
- [X] C Participation ✓
- D Elite

(Total for Question 4 = 1 mark)

58

5 Which of the following is a correct statement about flexibility? (1)

- A It is the ability to change the position of the body quickly
- B It is the ability to use two or more body parts together
- C It is the ability to retain the body's centre of mass over the base of support
- [X] D It is the range of movement at a joint ✓

(Total for Question 5 = 1 mark)

6 **Figure 1** shows a 200m butterfly swimmer.

Figure 1

Which of the following components of health-related exercise is **most** important for this performer in the last 25m of a race? (1)

- A Muscular strength
- B Body composition
- C Flexibility
- [X] D Muscular endurance ✓

(Total for Question 6 = 1 mark)

7 Which of the following components of skill-related fitness does the standing three-ball juggle measure? (1)

- A Speed
- [X] B Coordination ✓
- C Balance
- D Reaction time

(Total for Question 7 = 1 mark)

59

8 Which **one** of the following is a correct statement relating to the Harvard step test? (1)

- A It is used to measure muscular strength
- [X] B The result is based on heart rate readings ✓
- C It is used to test anaerobic fitness
- D The equipment required to carry out the test is a treadmill

(Total for Question 8 = 1 mark)

9 As part of a healthy active lifestyle, an individual should apply the principles of training in their personal exercise programme. Which of the following training methods is a shot putter likely to use if they are applying the principle of specificity to their training programme? (1)

- A Continuous training
- B Circuit training
- [X] C Weight training ✓
- D Interval training

(Total for Question 9 = 1 mark)

10 Which of the following is a correct description of 'progressive overload'? (1)

- A Matching training to the particular requirements of an activity
- B Making sure there is enough time between training sessions so that adaptation can take place
- C Increasing the intensity too much, causing injury to the muscle
- [X] D Increasing intensity a little more each week once your body has adapted to the previous workload ✓

(Total for Question 10 = 1 mark)

11 Which of the following is a form of interval training? (1)

- A Running for 30 minutes without a break
- B Holding a weight for 10 seconds, having a break and then holding the weight for another 10 seconds
- [X] C Run 100 metres, rest for 1 minute and do this for 10 reps ✓
- D Cycling 10 miles

(Total for Question 11 = 1 mark)

60

12 Which of the following is a correct statement relating to goal setting? (1)

- [X] A Goal setting can increase motivation. ✓
- B Goal setting can increase cooperation.
- C Goal setting can increase competition.
- D Goal setting can decrease reversibility.

(Total for Question 12 = 1 mark)

13 Which of the following is a measurable goal? (1)

- A To score more goals in netball
- B To be more accurate in shooting
- [X] C To run 5k 2 seconds faster ✓
- D To beat my rival in sprinting

(Total for Question 13 = 1 mark)

14 Which of the following is represented by the **R** in SMART goal setting? (1)

- A Reversibility
- [X] B Realistic ✓
- C Rest
- D Regular

(Total for Question 14 = 1 mark)

15 Which of the following should form the **smallest** percentage of macronutrients in the diet? (1)

- A Protein
- [X] B Fats ✓
- C Carbohydrates
- D Fibre

(Total for Question 15 = 1 mark)

61

16 Which percentage of their training threshold would a performer be working at if they wanted to improve anaerobic endurance? **(1)**

☐ **A** 60–80%

☐ **B** 50–60%

☒ **C** 80–90% ✓

☐ **D** 90–100%

(Total for Question 16 = 1 mark)

17 Explain how participation in physical activity can stimulate the development of friendships. **(2)**

...Joining a club or team can enable you to meet new people and make new friends. ✓ For example, an elderly person may feel lonely and join a club or team to make friends. ✓

(Total for Question 17 = 2 marks)

18 Give an example of the key influence 'image'. **(1)**

...Media ✓

(Total for Question 18 = 1 mark)

19 Brian has played tennis for 15 years but has injured his knee and cannot take part as a performer any longer. Explain how he could stay involved in tennis. **(3)**

...Brian could take part in tennis as a coach. ✓ He could use his experience to help give advice to others about their skills. ✓ Brian could also take part as an official and use his experience to umpire games of tennis. ✓

(Total for Question 19 = 3 marks)

20 Stanley has started attending exercise to music classes to improve his fitness.

Explain the relationship between exercise and fitness. **(3)**

...If you take part in regular exercise you can increase your fitness. ✓ For example, if you take part in continuous running you will increase your cardiovascular fitness. ✓ ✓

> You could be asked to describe the relationships between health, fitness and exercise in any combination.

(Total for Question 20 = 3 marks)

21 **Figures 2** and **3** show performers using balance.

Complete the table by explaining how balance would be used by each performer. **(4)**

Performer	How they use balance
Figure 2 Horse riding	Horse riders use balance to stay on top of the horse so they do not fall off. ✓ They have to adjust their position so that their centre of mass is over the base of support. ✓
Figure 3 Hammer throwing	Hammer throwers use dynamic balance. ✓ Without balance they would lose control and step out of the circle, leading to disqualification. ✓

(Total for Question 21 = 4 marks)

22 Anisha throws the shot. She would like to increase her muscular strength to improve her performance. She is following a personal exercise programme.

Explain how Anisha could use the FITT principle to improve her muscular strength. **(3)**

...Anisha could increase the amount of intensity by increasing the weight she lifts gradually during her programme. ✓ She could gradually increase the amount of time she trains for by 5 minutes each time. ✓ She could also increase the frequency of her training by increasing the number of times she trains each week. ✓

> The FITT principle is used as a guide to apply progressive overload.

(Total for Question 22 = 3 marks)

23 Describe the role of carbohydrates in a healthy balanced diet. **(2)**

...Carbohydrates provide the bulk of a healthy diet. ✓ They provide us with energy for activity. ✓

(Total for Question 23 = 2 marks)

24 Donna is coaching the under-16 football team and is planning to use fartlek training as a method of training. Evaluate whether fartlek training would be the most appropriate choice of training for all members of the football team. **(6)**

> Think about what the performer needs during a game.

...Fartlek training could be the most appropriate training method because improved cardiovascular and muscular endurance are both needed in football. ✓ It is very similar to the game situation where there is sprinting and recovery. ✓ For example, making a fast break to score a goal and then jogging back to position. It would allow the football players to work anaerobically and aerobically dependent on their position. ✓ Donna can apply the principles of individual differences by adapting the amount of jogging and sprinting performed dependent on the player's position. ✓ For example, an upfront player might have more sprinting in their training than a defending player. Other methods of training may also be appropriate for football players. Circuit training may be beneficial as this allows more emphasis on skills ✓ if required. It would also allow for a variation in the type of training completed. Cross training would also be appropriate for football players. Performers may find fartlek training boring, so circuits and cross training could provide variety. ✓

> Note that full credit can only be given where answers are developed with appropriate reasons and examples.

(Total for Question 24 = 6 marks)

TOTAL FOR PAPER = 80 MARKS

1 Which of the following is **not** a physical benefit of exercise?   (1)

- ☐ A   Improved fitness
- ☒ B   Improved self-esteem ✓
- ☐ C   Improved muscular endurance
- ☐ D   Increased strength

(Total for Question 1 = 1 mark)

2 Which of the following benefits is **most** likely to occur from taking part in team sports compared to individual sports?   (1)

- ☐ A   Increased competition
- ☐ B   Aesthetic appreciation
- ☐ C   Physical challenge
- ☒ D   Improved cooperation ✓

(Total for Question 2 = 1 mark)

Questions 3 and 4 relate to the key influences that impact on participation.

3 Which of the following is an example of the participation key influence 'culture'?   (1)

- ☐ A   Peers
- ☐ B   Family
- ☐ C   Status
- ☒ D   Disability ✓

(Total for Question 3 = 1 mark)

4 Which of the following describes a socioeconomic influence for taking part in exercise?   (1)

- ☐ A   I joined the local orienteering group as they meet near my house.
- ☒ B   I play golf at a private golf club as it is important how people see me and my business. ✓
- ☐ C   I cycle because I want to be as well known as Sir Bradley Wiggins.
- ☐ D   I have taken up hurdling because I saw it on the television.

(Total for Question 4 = 1 mark)

5 Niqa used to play football regularly, but due to an injury he now watches his children play instead. He knows a lot about the game and wants to get involved but is only available on match days. Which of the following roles could Niqa adopt?   (1)

- ☐ A   Coach
- ☐ B   Volunteer
- ☒ C   Referee ✓
- ☐ D   Performer

(Total for Question 5 = 1 mark)

6 Which of the following defines the term 'fitness'?   (1)

- ☒ A   The ability to meet the demands of the environment ✓
- ☐ B   A form of physical activity done to maintain or improve health and/or physical fitness
- ☐ C   A state of complete mental, physical and social well-being, not merely the absence of disease or infirmity
- ☐ D   Any form of exercise or movement

(Total for Question 6 = 1 mark)

7 Which of the statements below accurately describes when the performer would use cardiovascular endurance in their activity?   (1)

- ☐ A   A goalkeeper in the 81st minute of the match running off her line to make a save
- ☐ B   A rower at the start of the race
- ☐ C   A 100m sprinter towards the end of his race
- ☒ D   A tennis player during a long hard rally in the fifth set ✓

(Total for Question 7 = 1 mark)

8 Which of the following is the **most** appropriate method of training for a performer wishing to improve their cardiovascular endurance?   (1)

- ☐ A   Interval
- ☐ B   Weight
- ☒ C   Continuous ✓
- ☐ D   Cross

(Total for Question 8 = 1 mark)

9 Which of the following is **not** a component of the FITT principle?   (1)

- ☐ A   Frequency
- ☐ B   Time
- ☐ C   Type
- ☒ D   Target zone ✓

(Total for Question 9 = 1 mark)

10 Alana is a pentathlete, so she has to train to improve performance in fencing, swimming, shooting, running and show jumping. Which of the methods of training would be **most** suitable for her?   (1)

- ☐ A   Interval training
- ☐ B   Continuous training
- ☒ C   Cross training ✓
- ☐ D   Weight training

(Total for Question 10 = 1 mark)

11 Which fitness test protocol is being described below?   (1)

Stand side on to a wall, feet flat on the floor. Mark the highest point where the tips of your fingers can reach the wall. Jump as high as you can.

- ☐ A   Harvard step test
- ☐ B   Standing broad jump
- ☒ C   Sargent jump test ✓
- ☐ D   Standing stork test

(Total for Question 11 = 1 mark)

12 Which **one** of the following is a correct statement relating to the three-ball juggling test?   (1)

- ☐ A   Stand 3 metres away from the wall
- ☐ B   It is a test of reaction time
- ☒ C   Another person counts how many catches you complete ✓
- ☐ D   You can catch the ball with both hands

(Total for Question 12 = 1 mark)

13 Which of the following is a benefit of a warm-up?   (1)

- ☒ A   Focuses your mind ✓
- ☐ B   Increases lactic acid production
- ☐ C   Reduces the chance of injury after the activity
- ☐ D   Decreases blood flow to the muscles before exercise

(Total for Question 13 = 1 mark)

14 The graph in **Figure 1** shows suggested target heart rate zones depending on age.

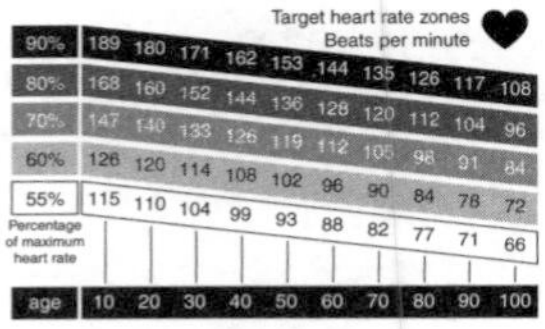

Figure 1

Using the information in **Figure 1**, which of the following is the most likely target heart rate zone for a healthy 20-year-old who wishes to improve their anaerobic fitness?   (1)

- ☐ A   200–220 bpm
- ☐ B   140–160 bpm
- ☒ C   160–180 bpm ✓
- ☐ D   110–180 bpm

(Total for Question 14 = 1 mark)

15 Planning what and when you eat is an important part of leading a healthy active lifestyle. Which of the following would be the **most** appropriate amount of time to leave before exercising after a large meal?   (1)

- ☐ A   Five minutes
- ☐ B   Half an hour
- ☐ C   45 minutes
- ☒ D   Over an hour ✓

(Total for Question 15 = 1 mark)

16 Which of the following nutrients provides energy for **both** anaerobic and aerobic activity? (1)

- [ ] **A** Fats
- [ ] **B** Protein
- [x] **C** Carbohydrates ✓
- [ ] **D** Vitamins

(Total for Question 16 = 1 mark)

17 Figure 2 shows the sports participation pyramid.

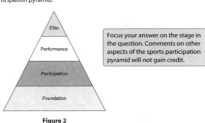

Figure 2

Focus your answer on the stage in the question. Comments on other aspects of the sports participation pyramid will not gain credit.

Using an example, describe the foundation stage of the pyramid. (3)

The foundation stage of the pyramid is the introductory stage. ✓ For example, a pupil taking part in gymnastics during a compulsory physical education lesson at school would be at the foundation stage. ✓ It is when the basic skills of gymnastics would be learned. ✓

(Total for Question 17 = 3 marks)

18 There are many initiatives to increase participation in sport. Describe **one** other common purpose of initiatives. (2)

To create opportunities for talented performers to achieve success, for example by providing funding for talented performers to help pay for their expenses. ✓ E.g. the World Performance Pathway initiative. ✓

Avoid giving more answers than asked for as they will not be considered and will waste time.
Try to include examples in 'describe' and 'explain' questions.

19 Goal setting is used to improve performance. Explain **one** reason why it is important that set goals are specific. (3)

It is important that goals are specific so that they provide focus for the performer in order to bring about improved performance. ✓ For example, a specific goal is to improve my 100m sprint time by 0.2 sec. ✓ If a goal is too vague the performer may not know when it has been reached. ✓

(Total for Question 19 = 3 marks)

20 Explain the term 'reversibility'. (3)

Avoid using question words to explain the terms in the questions, e.g. reversed in this case.

Reversibility may occur due to injury or a long holiday. ✓ Reversibility means that any improvement or adaptation to the body resulting in increased fitness, for example muscle hypertrophy as a consequence of regular weight training, will be lost if you have a prolonged break from training. ✓ In this case muscles will undergo atrophy. ✓

(Total for Question 20 = 3 marks)

21 Using an example, describe the purpose of a cool-down in an exercise session. (3)

A cool-down can consist of light exercise and stretching, ✓ e.g. a light jog around the pitch at the end of the match. ✓ The purpose is to help bring the heart rate and breathing rate slowly back down to resting rate. By maintaining light exercise this prevents blood pooling (and fainting) and aids the removal of lactic acid (through elevated breathing), helping to prevent muscle soreness. ✓

You could also mention improved flexibility by re-stretching muscles that have been contracting during exercise session.

(Total for Question 21 = 3 marks)

22 (a) Joel is a 100m sprinter. Before he begins his training he completes a number of fitness tests. Explain why the Illinois Agility Test would not be an appropriate test for Joel to undertake. (2)

The Illinois Agility Test would not be appropriate for Joel because during the 100m sprint he would not be using agility; ✓ the race is run on the straight section of the track, so there is no need to change direction quickly. Therefore the test would not be testing an aspect of fitness that Joel needs to work on to improve his performance. ✓

Ensure you link the response to the question.

(b) Explain a suitable test for Joel. (2)

Joel would benefit from testing his speed using the 30m sprint as this tests an aspect of fitness that is critical to his performance in the 100m. ✓ The 30m sprint is a good test of acceleration and speed. ✓

(Total for Question 22 = 4 marks)

23 Evaluate the importance of body composition for a boxer and a long jumper, giving examples of its possible effect on performance. (6)

Body composition is important to all performers as they need an appropriate ratio of body fat to muscle for their activity. ✓ A boxer needs to be able to move around the ring at ease, therefore they need a relatively low percentage of body fat. Body fat increases the boxer's weight, so if they had too much body fat they would find it harder to move around the ring and may get hit because they don't move out of the way quickly enough — enabling their opponent to gain points. ✓ Also, boxers are categorised by weight. Any additional weight (through fat stores) could mean they have to fight in a heavier weight category against someone who has more muscle than they do so can hit with more powerful punches, making them much harder to beat. Greater body mass/fat for a boxer could be advantageous as it would make them less easy to knock down. ✓

Long jumpers would also benefit from having a low percentage of body fat as they need to be able to manoeuvre over the bar without hitting it. ✓ If they have too much body fat it will be harder for them to gain enough height as there will be more weight leaving the ground, meaning they are less likely to clear the bar and get into the next round. ✓ Although it is important to have muscle to gain height, they also need to ensure they do not have too much body mass from fat or muscle so that their body is more streamlined, making it easier to clear the bar. Reduced mass around the joints will allow greater flexibility, allowing the performer to achieve the correct shape to clear the bar easily.

In conclusion, all successful performers must have an appropriate ratio of body fat to muscle for their activity. Too much or too little muscle or body fat can influence their ability to perform well. ✓

Ensure you provide examples from the specific activity to support responses.

Note that full credit can only be given where answers are developed with appropriate reasons and examples.

(Total for Question 23 = 6 marks)

TOTAL FOR PAPER = 40 MARKS

Published by Pearson Education Limited, Edinburgh Gate, Harlow, Essex, CM20 2JE.

www.pearsonschoolsandfecolleges.co.uk

Text and original illustrations © Pearson Education Limited 2013
Edited, produced and typeset by Wearset Ltd, Boldon, Tyne and Wear
Cover illustration by Miriam Sturdee

First published 2013

17 16 15 14 13
10 9 8 7 6 5 4 3 2 1

British Library Cataloguing in Publication Data
A catalogue record for this book is available from the British Library

ISBN 978 1 292 01377 0

Printed in Slovakia by Neografia

The publisher would like to thank the following for their kind permission to reproduce their photographs:

(Key: b-bottom; c-centre; l-left; r-right; t-top)

Alamy Images: epa european pressphoto agency b.v. 39b, Juniors Bildarchiv GmbH 64t, Ted Foxx 31, Tetra Images 40; **Getty Images:** Adam Pretty 16, AFP 52b, Christian Petersen 64b, Getty / AFP 7r, Julian Finney 39t, Lucidio Studio, Inc. 46, Yellow Dog Productions 5c, YURI KADOBNOV 39c; **Glow Images:** Image 100. Corbis 60, Image 100. Corbis. 56c; **PhotoDisc:** Jeff Maloney. 52c; **Shutterstock.com:** Christian Bertrand 4, Denis Kuvaev 5r, homydesign 37, Jack Dagley Photography 56r, Jose Gil 7l, Maxisport 5l, MISHELLA 52t, mooinblack 8, Pete Saloutos 25; **Veer/Corbis:** Nuiiko 56l.

All other images © Pearson Education Limited

Every effort has been made to trace the copyright holders and we apologise in advance for any unintentional omissions. We would be pleased to insert the appropriate acknowledgement in any subsequent edition of this publication.

In the writing of this book, no examiners authored sections relevant to examination papers for which they have responsibility.